S
CONNECTIONS
I
E
N
C
E

Projects for
Science and Technology
with Drama

from
Questions

WATTS BOOKS

London . New York . Sydney

First published in 1993 by Watts Books
96 Leonard Street
London EC2A 4RH

ISBN: 0 7496 1102 2

Dewey Decimal Classification Number: 507

10 9 8 7 6 5 4 3 2 1

Designed by: The Questions Publishing Company

Typeset by: The Questions Publishing Company

Acknowledgments
The publishers are grateful to the following for permission to reproduce photographs/prints:
French Government Tourist Office, p 17
The Environmental Picture Library, pp 32, 42, 45
Learning Through Action, pp 50, 52, 74, 75, 76
Mary Evans Picture Library, pp 54, 63, 65
National Blood Transfusion Service, p 66

Printed in Great Britain by The Bath Press, Avon

Contents

Introduction *Ken Byron*   **4**

SECTION 1: *EARTH, ROCKS AND ROADS*

Caving expedition *Ken Byron*   **8**
In role as geologists, young children learn about rocks and underground exploration.

Problems for Severus *Mike Potter*   **13**
In role as Romans and Britons, children investigate the invaders' technology.

The Mogul Dagger *Ros Smith*   **20**
A crime in a graveyard setting offers children the opportunity to observe different types of stone.

SECTION 2: *OUR ENVIRONMENT, YOUR ENVIRONMENT*

Pollution solution *Julie Hawksby, with Irene Heseltine*   **26**
Drama deepens children's understanding of a social problem caused by technology.

Jobs v. environment *Mike Littledyke*   **31**
Taking the role of those affected helps children weigh the arguments for and against technology.

People time forgot *Mike Littledyke*   **36**
Becoming a 'primitive' tribe helps children develop a questioning attitude to technology.

Being there *David Worley*   **42**
Children go on a drama expedition to investigate the destruction of rainforests.

SECTION 3: *IS LIFE GETTING HEALTHIER?*

Yesterday's children *Learning Through Action*   **50**
Nineteenth-century technology comes under scrutiny as children go into role as child labourers.

Epidemic *Nick Folkard*   **54**
Children step back into the nineteenth century to learn about factors affecting public health.

Dramatic discoveries *Mike Potter*   **63**
Learning about medical developments for work in role as pioneering medical scientists.

Script for some germs *Wendy Allen*   **68**
Improvisation and writing plays help children learn about germs and dental hygiene.

Gasping for breath *Learning Through Action*   **74**
Drama and research teach children about hazards to breathing both now and in the industrial past.

Index   **80**

Introduction

In a drama, we step into an imaginary situation (fictional context). The learning which occurs grows out of us being in that situation and having to respond to its pressures. Because drama situations are fictional, we are not restricted to 'real' contexts that can be set up in the classroom or on occasional trips. As the projects described in this book show, we can operate in any context we choose: for example, the properties of rocks can be investigated in the context of an expedition to explore a newly discovered cave system (see 'Caving expedition', pages 8-12), or the context of a police investigation into the theft of a missing stone ornament (see 'The Mogul Dagger', pages 20-24). And both the properties of rocks and the technological problems related to road and bridge building can be encountered in the context of the building programme the Romans undertook to subdue Britain (see 'Problems for Severus', pages 13-18).

❑ **Operating in role**

In drama, we operate in role and this has a number of important implications:

Pupils can come at the material in a different way from that of children in a normal learning situation. In the cave project, for example, the children's roles as experts undertaking a scientific investigation give status and motivation. In 'People time forgot' (pages 36-41), the children are invited to learn about the problems of environmental exploitation first in role as members of a 'primitive' tribe and then as the experts who will have some say in the exploitation of the tribe's territory.

Teacher and children can relate to each other in more ways than as teacher and children. In 'Caving expedition' (pages 8-12), the teacher can function as peer and colleague (expedition member); as someone uncertain how to deal with a problem, asking colleagues' advice: 'What if members of the public find the caves, damage them and hinder our work?'; and as opponent/devil's advocate (intruder in the caves who won't accept that s/he has any less right to be there than the geologists).

Children can relate to each other in a greater range of ways than is possible in 'real' situations alone. The fictional context of our task as geologists ('Caving expedition'), explorers ('Being there', pages 42-48) or members of a village community ('Jobs v. environment', pages 31-35) can create a powerful sense of group identity and collaborative endeavour. This is because drama creates real tasks for real purposes.

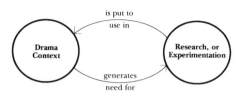

Fig. 1

Fig. 2

Fig. 3

❏ Making things matter

Talking about real tasks and purposes sounds paradoxical, after emphasising that drama is fictional. What it refers to is the power of drama contexts to make things matter. It mattered to the children in role as villagers in 'Jobs v. environment' to explore whether they could have much-needed jobs and at the same time preserve their tranquil environment. It mattered to the children in role as nineteenth-century doctors and townspeople in 'Epidemic' (see pages 54-60) to find out the causes of the disease that was sweeping through their community.

Because things matter, drama is a generative process in which one problem or need arises out of another.

❏ The need to know

Drama generates the need to know and provides a context in which existing knowledge can be put to use. The increasing intensity with which the children interrogated artefacts, pictures and written material in their drama sessions in the cave, and the steady incorporation of the results of this interrogation in the drama sessions, demonstrate this quite clearly. A beneficent cycle is set up, as shown in Fig. 1.

❏ Integrating the curriculum

In the traditional 'topic web', there is an attempt to include work on a variety of 'subject areas' within the topic (see Fig. 2).

Often the links between the different activities are rather tenuous, and are evident only to the teacher and not the children.

A drama context creates linkages in significantly different ways to the 'topic web'. Activities from a wide range of subject areas can be generated in a way that gives genuine coherence, because they arise out of the context and the children's role and activity within that context - so talk (of many different kinds), map-making, painting, research, estimation and measurement, the writing of journals, etc all arose logically and necessarily from the task set in 'Caving expedition', and the teacher's 'drama web' for the week is shown in Fig. 3.

❏ A social context for science

Drama can highlight the social context of science and technology. Much of the time on the caving project was spent using drama to motivate enquiry into certain aspects of the natural world. But when the oldest group found an intruder in the caves, a significant change of gear occurred. Science and technology, which investigate and harness the forces of the natural world, are human activities and take place in a social context. Social and political values, as well as economic forces, affect what is investigated or designed, and what is discovered or designed has effects on how we live. This group of children learnt that science has a social context when they were forced to deal with the question of public access to the caves.

It is important to recognise something about the way drama works - it deals in concrete human actions (the intruder's hand reaching to break off a stalactite); but the meaning goes beyond the specific act - it lies in the act's implications and its potential for the future. So, it is not simply damage by one person that is cause for concern, it is the realisation that such behaviour repeated could devastate the whole site. Because drama actions open up implications in this way, it means that drama context can very easily be used to explore the social, ethical, political and economic issues arising from scientific discovery or technological innovation.

❏ **Consolidating and communicating**

Drama creates opportunities for knowledge to be consolidated and communicated to others. For example, in both 'Pollution solution' and 'Jobs v. environment', much of the project was given over to 'finding out' about the pollution caused by industry. However, the hammering out of plans for dealing with existing pollution in the first project and the debates on whether or not to accept new industry in the second both offered a wonderful opportunity for the children to consolidate and organise their newly-acquired knowledge.

Finally, there is no greater test of one's knowledge and understanding than the (real) requirement to pass it on. Marshalling thoughts and information and communicating them orally, as well as in writing, are now important requirements of the English curriculum. And communicating thoughts and information orally, in writing and in diagrams and plans, is also a requirement of the science and technology curricula. The projects in this book offer many opportunities for this kind of work. For drama has, after all, an essential concern with communicating.

(This introduction has been adapted by the publishers, with Ken Byron's permission, from an article written by him in 1989.)

Section 1

Earth, rocks and roads

Caving expedition

The project described here was pursued intensively for a week in an open plan area (plus use of the hall space) and involved a school's whole infant base of three staff and sixty five- to seven-year-olds. The approaches outlined are equally valid for a longer-term, less intensive project, or for a single class, and could also be used with older children.

■ MONDAY MORNING

Stage 1: Sharing what we know

The project began with a whole base discussion on caves and caving: what we knew (a surprising amount) and sharing personal experiences, supported by a collection of books, pictures, slides, rock samples and borrowed potholing equipment.

Then, the class broke into separate groups.

❏ The youngest children worked on a long class picture showing different kinds of caves.

❏ The older children spent time looking at slides of cave exploration and discussed reasons for exploration.

Stage 2: Becoming 'geologists'

The children were told they were to do a drama in which they would become geologists. Geologists were defined as experts who knew about rocks and explored caves, but also as people who asked questions, looked carefully, tried out ideas and continually learnt something new (i.e. people who used a methodology to gain knowledge).

Then, the children were invited, in role, to recall previous expeditions they had been on. (This helped ease them into the role and allowed them to use information and concepts shared in Stage 1.)

Finally, a letter from the 'Director of the National Geographical Association (N.G.A.)' was read out to the groups, asking the geologists to report to his office, as he had an important task for them.

In role as a team of geologists, young children learn about rocks and underground exploration.

National Geographical Association

Exploring our world

This is to certify that

was made a member of the National Geographical Association on

Director

Signed

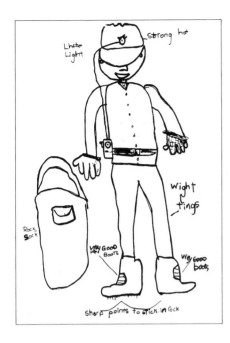

■ MONDAY AFTERNOON

The commission

An advisory teacher (could have been the head, parent, governor) took the role of the Director of the National Geographical Association, who then set the geologists three tasks:

- ❏ to explore a set of newly discovered caves
- ❏ to collect samples of the rocks they found there
- ❏ to record their findings and their work in a book.

Stage 3: Preparing for the expedition

The youngest group discussed the need to protect their heads and made caving helmets out of sugar paper. (Older children could have been set the problem of whether they could make from paper a strong, hard hat that really did keep them dry and protect them from bumps.)

A middle group discussed the needs of the expedition as a whole in order to prepare lists of equipment: for example, 'How are we going to find our way in the dark? By feel? By making sounds? By leaving a string to follow?' (Junior children could have investigated putting a light bulb on their hard hats and could have been introduced to the use of the magnetic compass.)

The oldest group did the same sort of work as the middle group, but also buttonholed the Director to question him about the nature of the task and about what the caves might reveal.

■ TUESDAY TO FRIDAY MORNING

Stage 4: Exploring, recording and researching

A very wide range of activities was encompassed - all of them organically linked by the context of 'exploring a new cave system'. Some examples from the work of the oldest group are offered here to give a flavour of the activities:

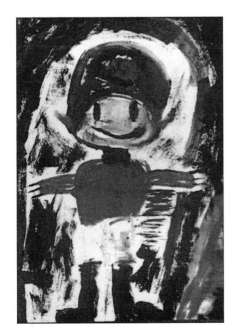

❏ Exploring

Stephen: 'Want to see what's down that tunnel.'

The geologists (class and teacher) crawled along the tunnel, one by one, and eventually stood open-mouthed at the sight of a 'cavern' full of stalactites and stalagmites. As well as discussing the formation of these, they commented on the difference in temperature between the cave and the world outside. What is the air like? Where does it come from?

Soon after, they discovered a deep pit and dropped 'pebbles' down, counting the seconds till the splash to estimate the depth.

❏ Research

Each day, time was allocated to examine books, slides of caves and rocks, rock samples etc. Children used their senses consciously to look at colour and texture, to find similarities and differences. They asked questions such as: How big? How heavy? How hard?

If a binocular microscope had been available, they could have looked at particles of rock.

Comparisons between the samples and their drama finds were

Fig. 1

Diary Dad &
Here is me going into the cave. the cave is going in and in and in I saw some Stalact it's and stalagmites in the cave in the cave it was dark there were three tunnels.

constant: 'That's just like my tunnel'. Scrutiny of the resource materials grew more precise, and the need to know more strong, over the three days. The knowledge gleaned was fed back into the 'drama discoveries'.

❏ Recording
Back at base camp (part of the classroom), very careful maps of the cave systems were drawn and the tunnels and caverns were named; diaries were kept of each day's events and discoveries, including measurements; drawings and paintings recorded the experiences too.

Ben's drawing and diary (Fig. 1) show his attempts to grapple with perspective. Asked why he had drawn the cave entrance with concentric lines of different colours, he replied, 'Because it's going in'.

❏ Problem solving
At one point, the children became very concerned in case the general public should find their site and impede their work or damage the caves. They decided to put a sign at the entrance. This offered an opportunity to investigate which colours would show up best on which backgrounds and how large the letters would have to be to be readable at, for example, 25 metres. It took 20 minutes to debate exactly what the sign should say. This 'wrestling' for the right words - to describe adequately their experiences in the cave - was very pronounced throughout the week.

❏ Motivation
John, a generally 'poorly-motivated' seven-year-old boy, unable to read or write, showed little interest in the project at first, but, as the week went on, he became increasingly involved. During one session, he announced that he had found some stalagmites he wanted to measure, picking up on a previous session where the class had been estimating the height of a tunnel. He reappeared some time later with his drawing: 'I've measured the stalagmites. Look at that one. It's ten high!'

Later, he and the teacher were waiting in a 'cavern' for the other geologists to return from exploring several tunnels. She asked him what he could 'see'. He spoke in detail about fossils in the rock, and next day spent over an hour carefully painting them, working voluntarily through playtime.

On Thursday afternoon, John borrowed a book to copy a picture, wanted to know what the words said (a very unusual request for John) and asked about the meaning of various words such as 'exploration'. 'Like what we're doing', was his observation.

■ FRIDAY AFTERNOON

Stage 5: Presenting the findings
On Friday afternoon, the Director of the N.G.A. arrived at the base camp to receive the records of the expedition. Each class presented them to him in the form of a large team 'book'. Much time was spent explaining the work and the findings to the Director, who then formally thanked the geologists for their work and presented them with a certificate, enrolling them all as members of the National Geographical Association.

Books

Cave Joanna Cole (**The Story of the Earth** series) Franklin Watts 1989,
ISBN 86313 984 1.

Caves Jenny Wood (**Jump! Nature Book**) Two-Can 1991,
ISBN 185434 012 3.

Rock Collecting Roma Gans (**First Sight** series)
A & C Black 1989,
ISBN 0 7136 3093 0.

Under the Ground Daphne Butler (**Take One** series)
Simon & Schuster 1990,
ISBN 0 7500 0285 9.

What's under the Ground? Susan Mayes (**Starting Point Science** series) Usborne 1990,
ISBN 0746 00357 9.

Inside the Earth Joanna Cole (**Magic Bus** series)
Kingfisher 1992,
ISBN 0 8627 2789 8 (Fiction).

Mik's Mammoth Roy Gerrard Victor Gollancz 1993,
ISBN 0575 05442 5 (Fiction).

Music

'Fingal's Cave' appears on Mendelssohn's Symphony No.3 by The Hanover Philharmonic Orchestra, Nimbus 1991 (CD - NI 5318).

Rock and fossil samples

Amethyst, 7 Orchard Close, Pocklington, York YO4 2EQ.
Tel: (0759) 304345.

Stuart A. Baldwin, Fossil Hall, Boars Tye Road, Silver End, Witham, Essex CM8 3QA.
Tel: (0376) 83502.

Stage 6: Further developments

Two classes developed the cave project further, in very different ways.

In the middle group, one child reported seeing 'something like paintings' on a tunnel wall, so the geologists' enquiries took a new turn. The paintings were examined and 'reproduced' in a variety of media - chalk, charcoal, mud, grass, twigs and flowers.

Later, talk arose about monsters that live in caves. This led to a drama session with the class in the role of monsters, indignant that they had to live in a cave because of people's intolerance of creatures who looked different from themselves.

A movement session was developed around the overture 'Fingal's Cave', and the next stage, had the end of term not intervened, would have been to look at a variety of stories - fictional and factual - about caves.

The oldest group were presented with a challenge in the form of a teacher in role as a member of the public who had accidentally discovered their cave system. When the geologists asked him to leave, he challenged their right to do so.

Dealing with an intruder was a demanding task, requiring the children to draw on the knowledge they had acquired during the project in order to:

❏ argue the importance of the work they were engaged in
❏ demonstrate the need to protect the site
❏ explain what dangers there would be to the public.

The teacher in role pushed the geologists to their limits before finally accepting their request to leave.

This led to discussions and plans about how to deal with the problem of public interest: how to balance the need to protect and preserve the cave system and to facilitate further research, with a recognition of the public's 'right' to know about and have access to the caves.

Plans started to emerge for converting part of the cave system into a geological museum with exhibition facilities and guided tours, and for raising money to protect and research the caves by charging for admission.

Unfortunately, time ran out as the end of term approached. Otherwise, the creation of the museum and opening it to the public (other children, parents, staff) would have provided a very fruitful further development which could have been used to bring in work on:

❏ design and technology
❏ economic awareness
❏ the language of presentation.

As it was, the exercise had already shown how a drama context can be developed and how that context can provide a genuinely integrated, generative learning experience.

Subject checklist

Science: learning about the earth - rocks, fossils, stalactites and stalagmites; observation and recording of materials and their properties.
Technology: designing and making protective clothing; displaying 'finds'; preserving caves from the impact of tourism.
History: early cave paintings.
English: making records of the expedition; putting up signs for visitors to the caves.

Exploring our world

National Geographical Association

57 Goldpenny Street, London WC1 5AX
Tel: 071 637 54311   Fax: 071 637 54375

Exploring our world

National Geographical Association

This is to certify that

_____

was made a member of the National Geographical Association on

_____

Signed   Director

Problems for Severus

Children divide into Romans and tribespeople to investigate the science and technology the invaders brought to Britain.

Severus Maximus has problems. As General, he is responsible for establishing an army presence here in the wilds of Britain. He has experienced men under his command. But, to start with, he is billeted in temporary shelter - a fortified wooden enclosure - with local people all around him.

A class could start on this project by making a model of the enclosure - wooden stakes to form a palisade on the perimeter and very basic wooden buildings in the centre - showing where the soldiers might be living in it. Alternatively, they might mark out a space that represents the enclosure in the classroom and work in it when they are in role as Romans, getting to grips with the challenges suggested here.

The children can then go into role as Roman soldiers. Some of them can be officers, some non-commissioned officers (NCOs) and the rest ordinary legionaries.

❑ What do they think of this posting?
❑ What do they think of the locals?
❑ What are their immediate needs?

They could talk this over in groups of mixed rank, and then the NCOs and officers could meet with Severus Maximus to help him to sort out his priorities.

■ FACING THE DANGERS

From this beginning, ideas to stimulate work in science and technology can flow. If the teacher is in role as Severus Maximus, then s/he can control the type of activities that the soldiers undertake. For example, if the pupils in role say, 'We think the local people are unfriendly. We're going to get attacked', it can be suggested that, 'We need a watchtower'. Groups of children can build simple watchtowers from art straws or paper, or they may suggest and try other materials from junk to construction kits. The models can be compared for suitability, for example:

❑ Is the tower stable?
❑ Is there enough space for a sentry on top?
❑ Is the sentry protected while still being able to see out?

From this, it can be seen that the ideas for science and technology work, suggested by the context of 'the Romans', are not new or unusual. The thread of the drama, however, can add urgency to the **need** for an activity; it adds extra interest to the **research** into what is appropriate; and it can provide a continuing **stimulus** to keep on task, with results (or problems) being reported to the group, using the protection of the role.

■ PRELIMINARY SURVEYING

Severus Maximus is concerned to establish a supply route for his camp, so that means building a road. He also needs to establish a strong base, so that means stone buildings for the camp. Both these projects will bring in discussion of what sort of land is suitable for construction and will involve surveying to see where such ground lies.

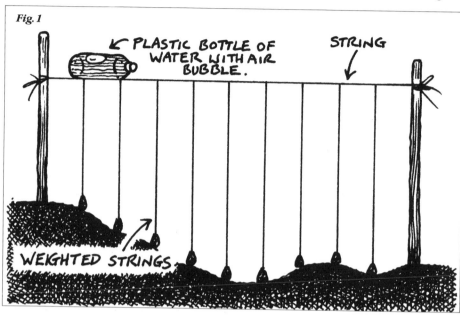

Fig. 1

PLASTIC BOTTLE OF WATER WITH AIR BUBBLE.

STRING

WEIGHTED STRINGS.

The Romans had their own version of a level (a device for finding out whether the surface of land is horizontal) and this was called a **chorobate**. The chorobate was like a heavy table with a trough on it. The trough was filled with water and as the chorobate was moved about, they noted how much the trough had to be moved to keep the surface of the water level.

If suitable books are available, children could read about the chorobate before going on to devise their own system for finding out how level or otherwise land might be. They can be challenged to come up with their own solutions to this problem, but one idea is to use a large, plastic drinks bottle rather than the trough of the Roman device. This can be filled with water almost to the top, but leaving an obvious air bubble. The children can plot the profile of a nearby piece of land using their level, two pieces of wood, string and some weights. The string is tied taut between the pieces of wood, up above the land to be measured. It must be tied at points that ensure that when the plastic bottle is drawn along it, the bubble stays in the same place. Then, strings can be dropped to the ground at intervals along the horizontal string and held taut by weights at the end of each. The profile of the land is shown by the position of the weights (see Fig. 1).

Before any building or road-making can take place, the hardness/softness of the ground must also be investigated, so another group of soldiers-cum-engineers could report back in role on what equipment they had devised to

ONE CHILD'S IDEA FOR A SOIL TESTER.

WEIGHTS

MEASURE HOW FAR STICK SINKS INTO SAND, SOIL AND PEAT

Fig. 2

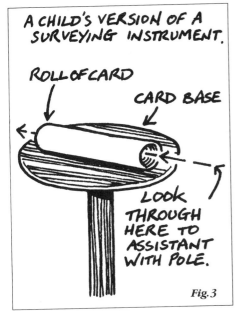

A CHILD'S VERSION OF A SURVEYING INSTRUMENT.

ROLL OF CARD

CARD BASE

LOOK THROUGH HERE TO ASSISTANT WITH POLE.

Fig. 3

measure ground hardness and the results of testing this equipment. Seeing how far a weighted stick sinks into the ground is an obvious test, and Fig. 2 shows a tool based on this idea.

The Romans kept the lines of their constructions straight by using an instrument called a **groma**. Can some children, as army engineers, make their own instruments to use for sighting straight lines? The basic requirement is to design and make an instrument that can take a sighting along a straight line. A cardboard tube fixed to a flat surface, which is in turn fixed to a stick can help here. Fig. 3 shows an instrument devised by a child to perform this function and Fig. 4 shows how a groma worked.

The General and the other soldiers should evaluate the work of their colleagues as each group presents its work, and they can, of course, challenge a group's findings and the accuracy of their devices.

■ GETTING THE WORK DONE

Severus Maximus is not going to use his own troops as road-building labour. He will summon representatives of the local tribespeople and tell them what he wants.

The class can undertake research on Roman roads, and the information they come up with can be used by Severus Maximus and his engineers to prepare themselves for a meeting with the leaders of the local tribe. At this meeting, the Romans must explain what road-building involves and what sort of jobs will want doing.

The tribal leaders can pass the information about the work they must do to their people.

❏　Will the tribespeople try to resist the work?

❏　Will they see benefits in the arrival of all this new technology?

❏　What arguments for and against co-operation can be put forward?

The children could test out the arguments on both sides, working in role as tribespeople and Romans.

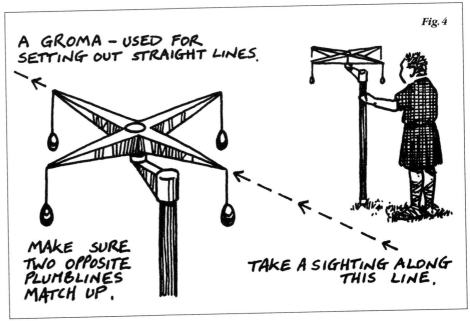

Fig. 4

A GROMA - USED FOR SETTING OUT STRAIGHT LINES.

MAKE SURE TWO OPPOSITE PLUMBLINES MATCH UP.

TAKE A SIGHTING ALONG THIS LINE.

Tribespeople: 'We must resist doing what the Romans tell us or we'll just be slaves.'

'If we do resist, they'll kill us.'

'Then they'll have no-one to do their work.'

'I think having the Romans here will improve our lives. We've never had anything like these roads!'

Romans: 'There's no way they can defeat us, once we get our camps and roads built.'

'What can we offer them that will get them to work for us without causing too much trouble?'

'They'll see they'd be better off with a civilised way of life, like ours.'

■ WATER SUPPLY

Severus Maximus has another problem. He wants to establish a water supply for his camp, and it will have to be protected from poisoning by his enemies. He can construct pipes to carry the water safely underground, but it must always be kept safe when it is travelling above the surface of the land (for example, when the land drops down into a valley).

The Roman solution was to have the water flow through **aqueducts** that were high up and could not easily be climbed.

Here the investigations children could undertake are concerned with structures and forces:

❑ bridge-building
❑ testing the strengths of arches
❑ devising a slope to keep the water flowing
❑ making the channel watertight.

Roman bridges and aqueducts were made of stone. Can your engineers devise machines that will lift stones up high? How will they be powered? Can they devise a treadmill that could utilise the power of several people for lifting really heavy weights?

To make walls and pillars, stones need to be fitted together. The engineers could use bricks or boxes to investigate the best 'bond' for stability. See Fig. 5 for bonds that have been developed for use with bricks and stones over the ages.

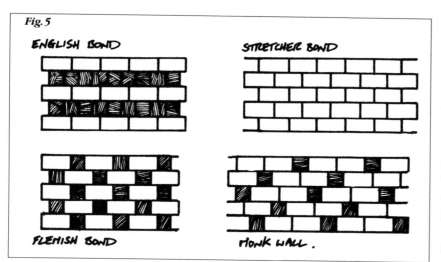

Fig. 5

ENGLISH BOND

STRETCHER BOND

FLEMISH BOND

MONK WALL.

What about concrete and mortar? The engineers could make up samples of brickwork using cement made of different ratios of sand and water (the Romans used lime, but that may be too dangerous) and test the samples for strength and hardness.

After the water has come to the fort, there could be a problem with dirty water. The engineers could look at ways of cleaning it, using **filtration** to stop the impurities getting through, or settlement tanks where the impurities sink to the bottom.

■ BACKGROUND SCENES

Throughout the project, interest in Roman engineering can be heightened by drama work with children in role as Romans and tribespeople. As well as the tribespeople meeting collectively, small groups can work on scenes among local families. For example, the head of a family may see many personal benefits in collaboration. He may be given gifts to supply labour. But they can all see more Roman settlers coming when the roads and towns and aqueducts have been built. And the wife may be worried that young people could be taken back to Rome as slaves if there are any uprisings and trouble.

■ OTHER SCIENCE AND TECHNOLOGY ACTIVITIES

❑   Make Roman style lamps. You could try vegetable oil floated on water with a string wick lying on it. The dim light of these lamps can be good for creating atmosphere at meetings, but **be careful they are placed out of participants' reach.**
❑   Design and make your legion's standard.
❑   Make maps and plans of the area of conquest. Where are the most suitable places for a camp to be sited? For a town to grow up? For roads and aqueducts to run?
❑   Design the layout and building for a Roman camp, taking account of the natural features of the area. Make a model of it.
❑   Write reports back to Rome to say how the various engineering works are progressing.
❑   Make and test equipment to defend the camp.

In a project like this, children can be presented with a challenge through the drama and can respond with investigations in science and technology. It may be necessary to go to reference material to check on facts where the historical aspect is important. However, this will help children to realise that science and technology have from the earliest times evolved in response to needs and not as isolated 'subjects' in some ancient text book.

Subject checklist
Science: learning about earth and rocks; properties of materials; use of forces in engineering.
Technology: the need to build roads; techniques of road building, bridge building etc.; devising simple machines for road building.
Maths: investigating straight lines and flat surfaces.
History: the Romans in Britain; their need to move troops and keep order among the people.

Books
Daily Life in Ancient Rome J. Carcopino (translated by E. Lorimer) Penguin 1991, ISBN 0 1401 2487 X.
Roman Britain Resource Book - pack of five titles (**A Sense of History** series) Longman 1992, ISBN 0 582 09292 2.
Roman Forts Margaret Mulvihill (**History Highlights** series) Franklin Watts 1990, ISBN 0 7496 0073 X.
Romans Nicola Baxter (**Craft Topics** series) Franklin Watts 1992, ISBN 0 7496 0762 9.
The Romans Anthony Marks and Graham Tingay (**World History** series) Usborne 1990, ISBN 0 7460 0340 4.

Posters and wallcharts
Roman Army posters (set of six posters) Oxford University Press 1991, ISBN 0 19 917129 7.
Roman Britain: Invasion and Conquest (E100) is available from **PCET**, 27 Kirchen Road, London W13 0UD. Tel: (081) 567 9206.

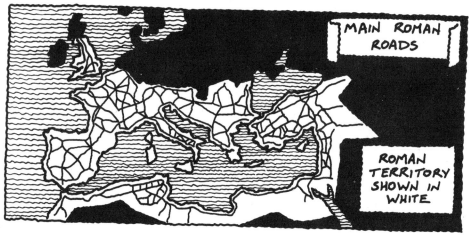

MAIN ROMAN ROADS

ROMAN TERRITORY SHOWN IN WHITE

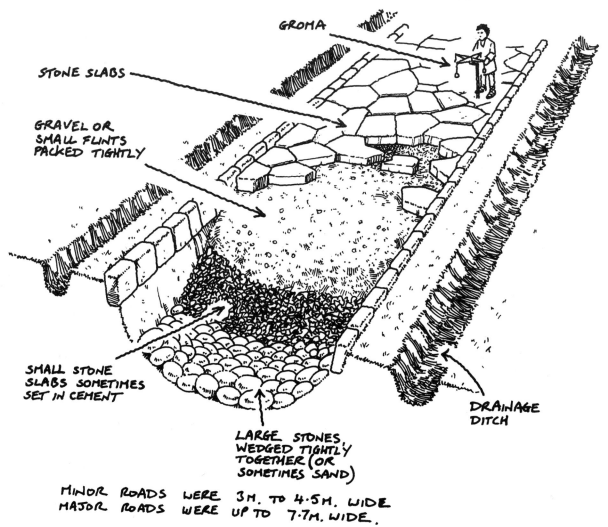

GROMA

STONE SLABS

GRAVEL OR SMALL FLINTS PACKED TIGHTLY

SMALL STONE SLABS SOMETIMES SET IN CEMENT

LARGE STONES WEDGED TIGHTLY TOGETHER (OR SOMETIMES SAND)

DRAINAGE DITCH

MINOR ROADS WERE 3M. TO 4.5M. WIDE
MAJOR ROADS WERE UP TO 7.7M. WIDE.

FACTFILE: STONES

LIMESTONE AND SANDSTONE

These are **sedimentary** rocks (formed from sediment which was first carried along by water and then deposited).

Limestone is made up of **calcium carbonate** from fossil shells together with pieces of more recent shells, fish bones, sand and mud. It has a fine-grained texture which is particularly obvious on weathered surfaces, and some types, including Portland stone, go white where the surface is washed by rain and black where the surface is more protected. Concrete, cement and plaster are all made from limestone.

Sandstone is made up of sand grains, and its texture can be coarse and gritty or quite fine. It is light in colour when new, but (in contrast to limestone) it turns black where it is exposed to the weather.

Most cities in the South of England have some buildings made of Portland Stone, whereas stone buildings in northern cities tend to be made of sandstone.

GRANITE

This is an **igneous rock** (formed by fire). Igneous rocks develop from a hot liquid called **magma**. Magma can cool down inside the earth, or flow out of the earth as **volcanic lava**. When magma or lava cools down, a rock is formed.

Granite is a popular building stone. It is made up of large crystals and is usually light grey in colour, though it can be pink, green or even orange.

MARBLE

This is a **metamorphic rock** (changed in form). It comes from limestone which has metamorphosed under heat and pressure. It appears in a wide range of colours, and starts with a beautiful sheen which it loses when it is exposed to the weather.

The Mogul Dagger

Investigating a crime in a graveyard setting offers children the opportunity to observe different types of stone.

The story of the theft of the Mogul Dagger was devised to overcome the problem of studying rocks in areas where there is a uniform bedrock (such as London Clay in Essex) or in urban environments where there is no ready access to a variety of rock types. A similar project could be undertaken with junior children in any area, provided a church with a suitable graveyard and an accommodating vicar can be found near the school.

■ ROBBERY AT THE OLD RECTORY

The story of a robbery, with a valuable stone hidden in a churchyard, was invented as a means of encouraging junior children to look closely at the different types of material used for gravestones. I also hoped that the realistic context of a police investigation would produce interesting recording work.

The project was introduced to the children using the following narrative (though another teacher might have chosen to take on the role of Inspector Granite):

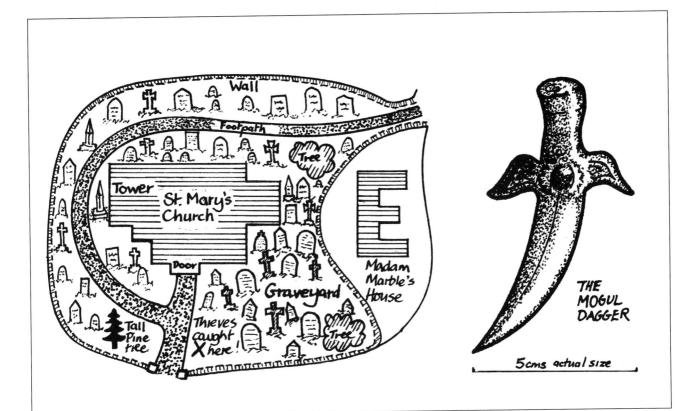

Map labels: Wall, Footpath, Tree, Tower, St. Mary's Church, Door, Graveyard, Thieves caught X here!, Tall Pine tree, Madam Marble's House, Tree

THE MOGUL DAGGER

5cms actual size

'Your class is on an outing to Rockwell Police Station. Whilst you are there, Inspector Granite, who is in charge of the Station, calls you into his office.

The Inspector explains that there has been a robbery at Madam Marble's house, The Old Rectory. Several valuable gems and stones have been recovered. However, the most precious object, the Mogul Dagger, is still missing. This is a dagger of greenish-grey semi-precious stone, set on one side with a precious gem.

You are to divide into small groups. Each group will be given a map of the churchyard and a copy of the statement made by the police officer who arrested the criminals. You will also need a notebook to record what you find, a hand lens, and a small plastic bottle of vinegar. If you put vinegar on rock and it fizzes, this means the rock contains lime. (You should only use the vinegar on pieces of stone that have come off a gravestone, or on a very small area of a gravestone that has already been seriously eroded by the weather.)

If the thieves disposed of the Dagger in the immediate area of the Church, they will probably have tried to camouflage it by hiding it in or near some other stone. You have to investigate the gravestones and the wall in a particular section of the church-yard. You must look carefully at each stone and, whether or not you find the Dagger there, you should write a report on your observations for Inspector Granite.'

PLACE		STONE	COLOUR	H/S	
CHURCH	WALL	FLINT	GREY/SHINY	HARD	:1
GRAVE	GOWERS	PORTLAND STONE	CREAM/GREEN	SOFT	:2
CHURCH	WALL	CEMENT	WHITE	SOFT	:3
GRAVE	WALDEN	GRANITE	GREY/BLACK/WHITE	HARD	:4
GRAVE	CHISNELL	SANDSTONE	BROWN	HARD SOFT	:5
GRAVE	EDWARDS	MARBLE	PINKY/WHITE	HR	:6
WALL	CHURCH YARD	BRICK	RED	SOFT	:7

PLACE		STONE	EROSION	AGE	
CHURCH	WALL	FLINT	NO	1000YRS	:1
GRAVE	GOWERS	PORTLAND STONE	YES – WHERE CARVINGS	84YRS	:2
CHURCH	WALL	CEMENT	YES	1000YRS	:3
GRAVE	WALDEN	GRANITE	NONE	46YRS	:4
GRAVE	CHISNELL	SANDSTONE	SOME	87YRS	:5
GRAVE	EDWARDS	MARBLE	HARD	34YRS	:6
WALL	CHURCH YARD	BRICK	YES	UNKNOWN	:7

■ THE CHALLENGE

There is the opportunity at the beginning of this work for discussion by the temporary police assistants of the tracks and trails the thieves might have made in the grass and undergrowth and for close observation of this natural area. When my class undertook the investigation it had snowed, which made the discussion of tracks and trails, including those left by animals, particularly interesting.

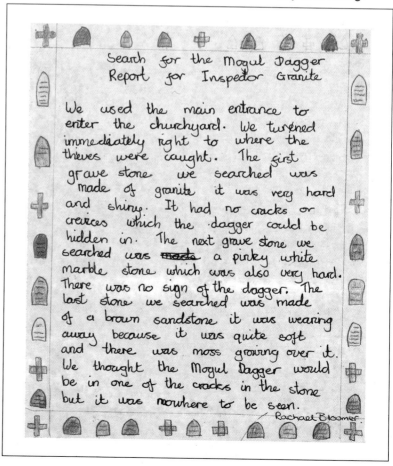

Search for the Mogul Dagger
Report for Inspector Granite

We used the main entrance to enter the churchyard. We turned immediately right to where the thieves were caught. The first grave stone we searched was made of granite it was very hard and shiny. It had no cracks or crevices which the dagger could be hidden in. The next grave stone we searched was ~~made~~ a pinky white marble stone which was also very hard. There was no sign of the dagger. The last stone we searched was made of a brown sandstone it was wearing away because it was quite soft and there was moss growing over it. We thought the Mogul Dagger would be in one of the cracks in the stone but it was nowhere to be seen.

Rachael Bloomer

Well wrapped up, the groups of children were sent to different areas of the large churchyard and set about their task.

I did not hide the Dagger until most of the work had been carried out. By this time the children were engrossed in closely examining the gravestones, although the alleged purpose of the exercise had not been forgotten. Observation using the hand lenses was showing that gravestones which looked greyish were in fact another colour or combination of colours. The lenses also helped the children distinguish what was stone with an eroded surface and what was lichen. Information gained by touching with hands was supplemented by making small rubbings, using crayon on paper.

The Dagger was found by a group at the bottom of a Portland Stone gravestone.

■ CLASSROOM FOLLOW-UP

Back in the classroom, the children took the notes they had made of their investigations and put the information gathered on the computer, using Inform Database. This allowed everyone to look at all the information gathered.

The 'fields' or headings indicated if the particular rock had been eroded, erosion being most easily seen where there were engravings. It was also possible, with most gravestones, to date them accurately. Another heading was used for giving a brief description of each gravestone and rock type. I helped with the naming of the rocks, although, as the children had already done some looking at different rock types, my assistance was not always required.

The computer work produced much discussion about rocks. The temporary police assistants were asked to write reports on how their investigations proceeded, and what they had noted, for Inspector Granite. And, as luck would have it, the Inspector particularly enjoyed these reports, because he was an amateur geologist!

Subject checklist
Science: investigating natural materials; observing the effects of weathering rocks.
Information technology: recording and sorting facts on a database.
Geography: learning about the formation of rocks and the effects of weathering on landscape.
English: report writing.

Books
Exploring Soil and Rocks Ed Catherall (**Exploring Science** series) Wayland 1992, ISBN 0 7502 0573 3.
Rocks and Minerals Kathryn Whyman (**Resources Today** series) Franklin Watts 1988, ISBN 0 86313 769 5.
Rocks and Soil Terry Jennings (**The Young Scientist Investigates** series) Oxford University Press 1982, ISBN 0 1991 8045 8.
Rocks Tom Mariner Cherrytree 1990, ISBN 0 7451 5049 7.

Useful addresses
Geological Society, Burlington House, Piccadilly, London W1V 0JU.
Rockwatch, The Green, Witham Park, Waterside South, Lincoln LN5 7JR.

Arresting officer's statement

Filled in by _____

Date _____

Following an urgent phone call, PC Slate and I found ourselves at The Old Rectory at 13.40 hours. From Madam Marble's statement, we learned that she had surprised burglars in the act of stealing some precious stones, including the famous Mogul Dagger.

After we took Madam Marble's statement, we immediately carried out a search of the area. Following some footprints, we arrived at the Churchyard, where a funeral had been taking place.

It turned out that the Sexton had seen some strange men mixing in with the people at the funeral, and so he and his choirboys and girls had apprehended them and locked them up inside the Belfry.

When we searched the men, the gems were all found except the famous Mogul Dagger. PC Slate and I searched everywhere in the Belfry, but could not find it, so we took the men back to the Station.

Section 2

Our environment, your environment

Pollution solution

The drama work described here was undertaken with infants. However, older children could also usefully investigate possible solutions to a local environmental problem in this way. With older children, the drama work could be combined with scientific tests to ascertain the degree of pollution, and there would be a more sophisticated use of language in the discussion and letter writing, but the main point of the drama - to deepen children's understanding of the issues involved - would remain the same.

■ RUBBISH

It is 27 September. I and my class of twenty-seven six-year-olds are three weeks into the new school year. Our science project, 'Rubbish', is growing in impetus and the problems of waste in the environment are becoming apparent to us. The children have suggested some solutions, but I feel that as yet their class answers are somewhat shallow and uncommitted.

We have spent half a day looking at waste in our local environment. During this time, we visited a tannery and walked along the river banks

Drama can be one of the best ways of deepening children's understanding of a social problem caused by technology.

above and below its site. On our return to school, the strongest recollection was of the smell of the Tannery, and then, during discussion, of the discoloration of the river downstream from it.

I explained that the Tannery had originally been sited on what was then the outskirts of a small village. It was the prosperity provided by the Tannery that had enabled the town to grow. However, the children's lack of maturity and experience led them to disregard the implications that the past had for the present. They suggested closing down the Tannery to eliminate the smell, the unsightly scene and the pollution of the area.

We have reached a point where the only way to deepen the children's understanding of the issues being raised is to enter a 'whole new environment'. It is time to start using drama as a tool to heighten awareness of the problems we are studying.

■ TAKING ON ROLES

As a first step, the class collaborated to produce a large map of the area we had visited, showing the sites of the Tannery, the town itself and the new housing development recently built on the outskirts.

I then divided the class into two groups, using (in this instance) eye colours: blues and non-blues. (Using colour, shoe types, house numbers etc. works equally well in producing mixed groups, and using these categories reinforces the important concept of classification at the same time.)

One group established themselves as Town Dwellers; and remembering the things they had seen on their visit, the members of this group drew plans and pictures of their houses, chose occupations and became family members.

(I pointed out to them that choosing adult roles would give them greater influence when decisions were being made.)

The second group made similar choices, but took on the roles of

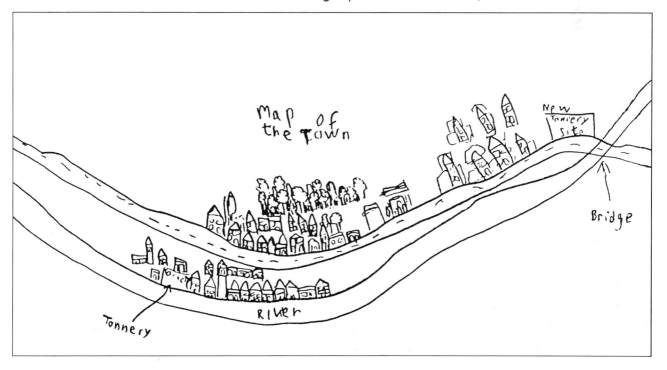

Newcomers to the area who had bought expensive houses in the new housing development. The scene was now set, and we waited eagerly to get to work during our next period in the Hall.

I asked the children to join me in a circle. They did this, but all the boys were on one side and all the girls on another, a recipe for disruption in my experience. So I named all the boys 'oranges' and all the girls 'apples', then asked the children to sit alternately 'orange and apple'. (The circle can also be ordered according to the numerical sequence of the children's house numbers, or birthday months. It is getting a 'mix' that is important.)

In our circle, we started to talk about what the children's own perceptions of drama were. As teacher, I accepted all these ideas to encourage the children to put into words their thoughts, beliefs and feelings. This confidence-building is vital when working with drama.

In summarising the children's ideas, I suggested that drama was making a story, a special story belonging only to us, in which all our words and actions counted towards the final outcome and in which we were all equal. We then agreed to go back into the roles of the two groups of people in the town. (I find that this verbal contract is essential.)

I explained to the children that when our story began and they became the people they had drawn and written about, then I too would be a different person. As this was a new concept for them, I told them that they would know when I was in role because I would wear my jacket. (With young or inexperienced children, a visible clue such as a hat or jacket helps.)

■ OPENING UP THE PROBLEMS

The children left the circle and became very active, forming family groups, establishing a daily routine, acting out their jobs etc. Some of the Townspeople, men and women, worked in the Tannery. The Newcomers, using the other half of the Hall, also went about their business.

After allowing time for the children to establish their roles, I entered in my own role as Mayor of the town, having chosen Brian as my Chief Advisor. (Every class has at least one potentially disruptive Brian; and giving this child an important role, close to the teacher, helps towards a more successful drama.)

As this was the first time the children had seen me working in role, their commitment wavered and some started to laugh. I stopped the drama and, removing my jacket, became the teacher again. I drew the children's attention to our agreement to become the people of the town and asked why they were failing to do this. This led to a discussion about how some children were working hard to stay in role, and how others must recognise, respect and value this by trying to stay in role too.

The children settled down and, again in role as Mayor, I told them that I had received several letters from people in the town complaining about the Tannery:
- ❏ that it smelt bad
- ❏ that it polluted the river
- ❏ that its site was very unpleasant to look at
- ❏ that heavy lorries carrying skins to it were becoming a nuisance.

(The use of letters, anonymous or otherwise, is a useful strategy to introduce problems that the children may not have recognised themselves.)

On hearing of the complaints, most of the Townspeople and all of the Newcomers agreed that the Tannery should be closed and the site used to build something of benefit to the whole community. We then left the Hall and went back to the classroom. We again split into the two groups, with each group suggesting ideas for the use of the land. (It was a conscious decision to keep the same groups so that the commitment to role and bonding of the groups would be strengthened.) The children drew pictures and maps to go with their suggestions.

- ❏ The Townspeople's final decision was an adventure playground and toy shops.
- ❏ The priority for the Newcomers was a sports centre and library.

I accepted and discussed all these ideas from the children. Along with the drawings, each group came up with a list of reasons to support their choices.

■ ENTER THE TANNERY OWNER

When the next Hall time arrived, the children and I sat in the circle and again made an informal verbal contract to reassume the roles of the community of Townspeople and Newcomers. I told the children that this time I would take the role of the Owner of the Tannery. The children assumed their previous roles, while Brian, as the Mayor's Advisor, read a notice of a meeting to be held between the people and the Tannery Owner. (The notice had been prepared in advance, and Brian had had a chance to practise.)

At the meeting, the Tannery Owner explained that he understood the concern about pollution, but he had three important points to make:
- ❏ The Tannery had originally been built on the outskirts of the village, and as a direct result of its presence the town had grown around it. (The Owner noticed some of his workers in the audience and greeted them individually, thus emphasising their close link with the Tannery.)
- ❏ Although the river was discoloured by the waste from the Tannery, the water had been filtered so that it did not harm any wildlife in and around it.

❏ The closure of the Tannery would be unthinkable because so many people, indeed most of the town, depended on it for their livelihood.

However, the Owner was willing to do what he could to help. Since the present buildings were getting old, he would be prepared to move the Tannery to another site. There was even a suitable field upstream, further from the town centre, near the new housing estate.

There was a lull while the Townspeople and Newcomers realised the implications of this move. The meeting was adjourned so that the two groups could talk about the new proposals. As teacher, I talked to both groups, helping them to clarify their thoughts. The meeting was then recalled so that both sides could put their viewpoints across.

■ FINDING THE RIGHT SOLUTION

The Townspeople supported the move, as it would solve their problems of pollution and make the land available for the adventure playground. They pointed out that living in the town meant that they had only small gardens.

The Newcomers were now against the move, because of the proximity of the site to their homes. They saw it as simply transferring the pollution problem from the town to their area.

Discussions with the Tannery Owner then moved on to solving the problems of smell and unsightly view for the Newcomers. It was suggested that:
❏ as there was plenty of room, the new site could be screened by growing trees.
❏ a building put up now could use the latest technology; and if the Town Council, on behalf of all the people of the town, shared the expense with the Owner, a new kind of chimney could be built that would eradicate the smell.

With agreement on these solutions, the meeting closed and the drama ended. Back in the class, the children worked as one group on some follow-up activities: researching and selecting appropriate trees for the screen, and writing letters that might have been sent to local nurseries to ask for advice and costs for planting it.

As a class, the children had accepted the Tannery Owner's position where they had not been ready to accept mine as Teacher, even though we had stated the same facts about the Tannery's siting and importance. It was obvious from the questions and discussions that the children now had a much deeper understanding of the issues than they had had prior to their drama experience; and they had been stimulated to look for more sophisticated solutions than simply closing the Tannery down.

Subject checklist
Science: looking at the effects of industry on the environment; the production and effects of waste materials.
Technology: planning for the use of land; finding ways to get rid of industrial waste.
Geography: mapping a built-up area; how the different sections of a town develop.
English: using books for research; debating and summarising arguments.

Books
Domestic waste and Industrial Pollutants Hugh Johnstone (**Facts On** series) Franklin Watts 1990, ISBN 0 7496 0125 6.
Ponds, Rivers and Lakes Anita Ganeri (**Ecology Watch** series) Evans Brothers 1991, ISBN 0 2375 1207 6.
Rivers and Lakes Brian Knapp (**Caring for Environments** series) Simon & Schuster 1991, ISBN 0 7500 0842 3.

Software
ILECC, John Ruskin Street, London SE5 0PQ produces River Studies (Code: 1102). Available for RM Nimbus, BBC, Archimedes and IBM systems.

Useful addresses
National RiverWATCH, Bayfordbury Field Station, Lower Hatfield Road, Hertford SG13 8LD.
Water Services Association, 1 Queen Anne's Gate, London SW1H 9BT.

Jobs v. environment

The following project offers ways of tackling the themes of conservation and pollution and also brings in economic awareness. The central dilemma on which the project is based is whether to preserve a pleasant village environment or to increase employment pros-pects by bringing in industrial activity which may damage that environment in several ways.

When technology brings both benefits and disadvantages, taking on the role of those affected helps upper junior children weigh the arguments.

In educational drama, the direction the project takes is best developed from the responses of the children to the subject matter. The most productive role for a teacher is a flexible one: taking a character role where appropriate, and acting as director and questioner at other times.

The project on conservation versus employment was developed with various upper junior groups over periods of several weeks, and each time it took a different form and direction. In each case, the motivation and involvement of the children were high, resulting in valuable learning experiences and the development of a wide range of skills.

■ SETTING THE SCENE

A fictional village is developed and the children go into role as families living there. This is a community where the environmental quality of life is high, but many members (one in four adults) experience the problems of unemployment, perhaps because of the closure of a woollen mill or other light industry plant a few years previously.

The building up of the village can use some or all of these strategies:

Setting up families
❑ Pupils form groups of 4-6.
❑ Pupils take roles of characters in a family and give names, ages, relationship and what each does for a living (including unemployed).

All should be adults so that they have responsibility in the drama.

Groups show scenes of family life to illustrate a typical day, e.g. evening meal time, reflecting on the day.

❑ Groups give a short account of family history.

❑ Pupils write diaries of the characters. (These can be continued throughout the drama.)

❑ Pupils make drawings (or find photographs) of the family houses.

Describing the village

❑ Pupils give the village a name.

❑ A map is made. As a class, pupils decide on the position of important features and let individuals draw them on. Map includes roads, street names, river, important buildings, family houses, names of nearest towns or villages etc.

❑ Working from the map, a model of the village is made.

❑ Pupils enact scenes of village life, e.g. in the street, pub etc.

❑ Drawings are made of scenes in the village.

❑ Interviews with villagers and reports of village life are done for the local newspaper.

In building this picture of village life, it is particularly important to draw out the problems associated with unemployment along with the benefits of life in a village with a relatively clean environment.

It is important not to rush the development of this part of the drama as it is a belief-building stage and will set the scene for the introduction of the central problem (the 'dramatic tension').

■ INTRODUCING THE PROBLEM

There are plans to build an agrochemical plant in the village. (Other topical examples - a toxic waste disposal plant or a nuclear reprocessing plant - could be used.) The benefits of jobs and increased opportunities for local business must be balanced against possible disturbance and even damage to the village and the area. The introduction of this idea is best done in stages to allow the issues to be fully explored.

Introducing the idea

❑ A rumour is started about the proposals (by teacher in role as villager).

❑ A report of the rumour is printed in the local newspaper. (Children can use the headlines on page 35).

❑ A councillor (teacher in role) is questioned, but makes no comment.

❑ The resulting discussions of villagers are overheard.

Making the proposals public

❏ The Councillor is interviewed again and confirms that the Council is to consider the plans and make a decision on whether or not to give planning permission.

❏ Modifications are made to the map or model to show the implications of the proposal.

❏ A front page news report is published.

❏ Further discussions between villagers are overheard.

■ THE RESPONSE TO THE PROPOSALS

A number of reactions for and against the proposals may arise which can be fully explored in the context of the drama.

Arguments for and against

❏ Pupils carry out research on pollution issues to inform the drama. What happens if waste from the plant gets into the local river? What happens if there are harmful emissions into the atmosphere?

❏ Newspaper reports on pollution issues are written.

❏ Pupils carry out a local traffic survey on a relatively quiet road. This is used as a measure of traffic flow in a village. A percentage increase (say 50 per cent) in the number of heavy goods vehicles can illustrate the possible increase in village traffic.

❏ A public meeting is held in the village hall with speakers for (factory representatives) and against (environmental group representatives) and with questions from the floor. The teacher in role could put both view-points. Alternatively, two groups of six or so children can represent the speakers. The children in each group support each other by taking turns to make statements and answer questions.

❏ News reports appear with interviews of villagers for and against the proposals. It is useful to get children to interview each other in pairs for practice, taking both viewpoints in turn to enable them to present both sides of the argument.

❏ Activities are organised to support viewpoints: letters to the local MP, council, etc.; loudspeaker van touring the village; petitions with villagers signing or declining to sign; posters and banners painted; marches by groups for and against the factory with petitions handed in to the council.

■ ISSUES ARISING FROM THE DRAMA

Issues may arise from class discussions or from action within the drama, but in either case, they will draw on the children's research. Looking at village life before the proposals, advantages quoted may include:

    a sense of community

    a clean, attractive environment with limited traffic

    a sense of history and tradition.

The disadvantages of so many being unemployed may include:

    lack of money for food, clothes, travel etc.

    low status, low self esteem and depression

    lack of sense of purpose and opportunity.

When the class looks at the implications of the proposals, possible advantages may include:

the availability of jobs

increased trade from secondary services increasing the wealth of the area

possible usefulness of products such as fertilizers and pesticides.

The disadvantages that may be brought up include:

potential pollution of the local environment from accidents or build-up of toxins from waste disposal (e.g. via smoke emissions or via river)

potential damage to people (e.g. increased incidence of cancer) and wildlife. (A consideration of the build-up of toxins in food chains is relevant here.)

possible harmful effects on society in general of products manufactured growth of the village, with the loss of the advantages of village life.

■ CLIMAX

A suitable climax to the drama is to enact a scene where the decision of the Council is announced to the villagers gathered outside the council offices. Afterwards, the villagers can describe how they feel the decision will affect their lives. Both possible decisions, for and against, can be enacted, to allow the children to experience the possibilities in each and to make their own choice if they so wish.

Having worked through the drama, it can be valuable to present the whole series of events in shortened form as a news broadcast or documentary feature which can then be shown to an audience. The children can take the roles of the presenters, reporters, villagers, councillors etc. This gives a strong sense of purpose to the drama as children love to perform to other groups, and also helps to consolidate what has been learnt. The audience can be asked for a show of hands to make the final decision on behalf of the Council and the final scene can reflect that decision.

Subject checklist

Science: researching the effects of chemicals on land, plants, pests and diseases, bringing in food chains and toxic build-up; pollution caused by factories; pollution caused by traffic.

Technology: making a model of a village; designing and producing posters and banners.

Geography: making a map; considering the social and economic aspects of life in a village.

English: writing diaries, newspaper reports and letters; presenting and summarising arguments.

Maths: traffic survey.

Information sources

The media regularly report on specific environmental debates and these reports are a major source of information for this topic. Other useful sources of information include:

Greenpeace: 36 Graham Street, London N1 8LL.

Friends of the Earth: 26 Underwood Street, London N1 7JQ.

Central Electricity Generating Board, Department of Information and Public Affairs, Sudbury House, 15 Newgate Street, London EC1A 7AU.

UK Nirex Ltd, Curie Avenue, Harwell, Didcot OX11 0RH.

Ministry of Agriculture, Food and Fisheries Publications, London SE99 7TP.

Food Sense, London SE99 7TT.

British Agrochemical Association, 4 Lincoln Court, Lincoln Road, Peterborough PE1 2RP.

ICI Agrochemicals PLC, Fernhurst, Haslemere, Surrey GU27 3JE.

National Farmers Union, Agriculture House, Knightsbridge, London SW1.

The Village Post

Your local news every week

40p

GIANT PLANT TO BRING NEW JOBS?

DEMAND FOR EXTRA BUSES

FLOWER SHOW with photos of the best exhibits

SOCIAL DIARY

FARMING

LOCAL NEWS

REGIONAL NEWS

AROUND & ABOUT

ENTERTAINMENT

FORTHCOMING EVENTS

People time forgot

Entering into the society of a 'primitive' tribe can help children develop a questioning attitude to technology.

The idea behind this drama project is to create a society which has had no exposure to the modern world. Those taking part in the drama will examine the technology of such a culture, and see what could happen when the society is 'discovered'. In this way, they can explore and consider the questions:

❑ What is technology?
❑ What are its origins?
❑ What are its functions?
❑ What are its purposes?

The drama framework could be used to support topic work on people such as Aborigines or American Indians. A drama approach compels children to research their topic. This encourages independent learning and expands geographical, historical and anthropological knowledge.

■ TO SET THE SCENE

Discuss with the children the idea of a tribe whose technology uses only natural, readily available materials and which lives in balance with the environment. The children can consider what the natural materials are that are available in their own environment, and then move on to thinking about how different a society would be if only these materials were available.

❑ Where might such a society be found?
❑ What tools and materials would be available to its members?
❑ How would they ensure that their environment could still supply their needs in the future?

Introduce a newspaper headline, 'The People that Time Forgot'. Say this headline was about such a tribe, which was 'discovered' after living isolated from the developments of modern society. (Discussion of Western bias concerning the use of the term 'discovered' is appropriate here.) Explain that the purpose of the drama is to create such a tribe and its culture and to see how it may be affected when it is 'discovered'.

■ CREATING THE TRIBE

1. Identity
The children are members of the tribe, which is made up of family groups (four to six in a group). Each child takes his or her individual name from an animal and puts a suitable adjective with it. Each family has a family name taken from a non-living part of nature. Thus an example of a tribal name might be 'Swift Deer from the family of the Moon'.

Totems are made as artwork to symbolise the family. They can be arranged at a central point to symbolise the tribe as a whole.

2. Environment
After discussion of what the environment of the tribe might be like, the children should create a map showing features such as forest, lake, river, waterfall and open grassland. The map needs to offer a location for the village which is obviously isolated. A site such as a large, extinct

volcano (like Ngorongoro crater in East Africa) with steep sides and difficult access could give a reason for isolation. Or the site could be reached through a labyrinth of caves, which only the elders of the tribe know the way through.

Decide on the type of dwellings. These might be huts made of mud or branches, or tents made from animal skins, but they should be made out of materials the map suggests are to be found in the area.

Decide on the animals and plants which you would find here. This is an opportunity for children to bring in favourite exotic animals, provided their habitat is similar to that shown on the map; but some animals could be imaginary. Ask the children to draw some of the animals and plants.

Discuss how the environment provides for the tribe: e.g. shelter, tools, food, water. This can lead into discussion of what might make the area of interest to people outside: precious stones and gold, oil, a previously unknown material which can provide limitless energy (this suggestion was made by one of my pupils following a previous discussion about uranium), useful types of wood, and a rich array of newly discovered plant and animal species (including a plant which can cure all forms of cancer).

3. Daily life

The children should work at building up a picture of how the members of their tribe spend their days; for example:

❑ How do they find their food?
❑ Do they grow plants?
❑ Do they tend animals?
❑ Do they hunt animals?
❑ What tools and materials do they use
  to make clothes?
  to build shelters?
  to cook?
  to farm?
  to fish?
  to hunt?

There is scope here for making models using the natural environment around the school, e.g. stones, sticks and grasses for binding; clay for making utensils. The older the children involved in the drama are, the more sophisticated can be the comparisons they make with their own society as they undertake this work.

Ask the children to develop scenes showing different aspects of life: obtaining food, cooking and eating, making implements and clothes etc. Discuss how the technology they come up with is appropriate to the needs of the tribe. Consider whether they only take what they need, using everything to the full and with minimal waste being naturally recycled.

4. Religion and folklore

Create names for gods and goddesses, taken from nature, and make drawings and models of them. Discussion of why the tribe would worship such deities could bring in the meaning of worship in general, and how it affects the relationship with the environment in particular. The children can then try inventing a religious and moral code (like the ten commandments) which will foster a harmonious relationship between the tribe and its environment.

The children can make their own musical instruments from natural materials (as far as possible). String, fishing line or elastic can simulate animal gut for plucked instruments. Straws can simulate reeds, and various cylinders can simulate hollowed wood for pipes. Use the instruments in scenes where the tribe worship the gods and goddesses, celebrate a birth/death, ask for success in the hunt, etc.

Finally, the children can create stories and songs to build up the

mythology of the tribe, e.g. origins of animals and plants, or stories involving gods and goddesses. They can tell or sing these around the evening fire.

■ DISCOVERY

When the scene is set and the children are able to believe in their tribe, it is time to move on to the discovery stage. To do this, I suggest that an explorer stumbles across the tribe after getting lost.

Initially a lost object (e.g. a tin opener) is found by a member of the tribe. No-one in the tribe has ever seen such an item before, and there is a discussion about its possible source and what to do with it. Then the explorer appears.

As teacher in role, I enter speaking German. The idea is that the tribal language is different from the explorer's. Communication is thus initially without words, which can lead to some very creative efforts by children.

The explorer is taken into the tribe and learns their language and way of life. However, when he or she decides to return to the modern world, we reach the culminating part of the drama.

■ CONSEQUENCES

Discussion of the consequences of discovery is now necessary. Who would be interested in the tribe and the resources of its environment? A number of interested parties have emerged from such discussions, including:

❑ conservationists who want the area and the tribe to be protected
❑ scientists who wish to study the living and non-living environment
❑ anthropologists who wish to study the life of the tribe
❑ media people (journalists, television crew) who wish to report the story of the tribe and the explorer
❑ mining companies who wish to exploit the resources of the area (e.g. oil, precious stones and gold)
❑ logging companies who wish to extract profitable timber
❑ medical research teams who wish to develop the medical properties of local resources (e.g. the cancer-curing plant)
❑ tour operators who wish to convert the area into a tourist centre.

At this point in the drama, the children change roles and become members of a government working party from the country to which this area belongs. It is their job to decide who from the above list is to have access to the tribe and the tribal area.

The consequence of allowing these interested groups to have access can be explored by conducting interviews with representatives of each.

Books
Aborigines Henry Pluckrose
ed. (**Small World** series)
Evans Brothers 1981,
ISBN 0 2376 0235 0.
Eskimos Jill Hughes (**Find Out
About** series) Evans Brothers
1991, ISBN 0 2376 0177 X.
**First Books of American
Indians** series including *The
Apaches and Navajos*
ISBN 0 5311 0743 4, *The
Iroquois* 0 5311 0747 7 Craig
Doherty, *The Totem Pole
Indians of the Northwest*
0 5311 0750 7 Don Beyer, and
The Sioux 0 5311 0754 X
Elaine Landau, Franklin Watts
Inc. New York 1989.
*On the trail of the American
Indians* Nicolas Grenier
(**Pocket Worlds** series)
Moonlight 1988,
ISBN 1 8510 3039 5.
The Children from Tibet Bodil
Hagbrink Blackie 1991,
ISBN 0 2169 3052 9 (Fiction).
Deserts and Jungles Marie
Farre (**Pocket Worlds** series)
Moonlight 1991,
ISBN 1 85103 134 0.
Life in the Mountains
Catherine Bradley (**Jump!
Ecology Books**) Two-Can
1991, ISBN 1 8543 4141 3.

Teacher or children can take on the roles of interviewers and interviewees. If it is too demanding for one person to answer in a role, others can assist by answering for the representative when he or she is stuck for words. An empty chair with several children available to answer for an imaginary occupant also works.

Scenes of the tribal area after a particular group has had access can be created in between the interviews, or when all the interviews are over, to illustrate the possible consequences. Throughout this phase in the drama, the impact of the modern world and its technology on the tribe and its environment can be fully explored. The benefits and potential harm to the tribe, the environment and the outside world need to be considered in each case.

■ CONCLUSION

After considering the likely consequences of the various groups' requirements, the government working party decides who will be given access to the tribe and its environment.

On the basis of these decisions, it is now possible to look at the combined consequences of the access of the successful interested groups on the tribe and its environment. Scenes as photographs (with children in 'still image' form) are an effective way of showing this. Characters in the photograph can be questioned on their part in the scene.

Returning to the headline 'The People that Time Forgot', the children can now write the article that goes with it. By this time, they will have had a rich experience of the meaning and significance of two types of technology, the so-called 'primitive' and the so-called 'advanced', in an original human context, and they will have considered the benefits and potential dangers of both for individual groups of people and for the planet as a whole.

Subject checklist
Science: considering conditions necessary for human life; the properties and uses of natural materials.
Technology: consideration of what technology is and how it varies according to place and time; designing and making artefacts from natural materials.
Geography: inventing a geographically realistic environment; understanding how the environment is exploited.
Religious education: investigating the nature of worship.
Music: composing and performing.
English: looking at communication without words; debating and summarising arguments; writing reports.

Using natural materials

For thousands of years, people made everything they needed from natural materials they found in their environment. In a few parts of the world, people still do this.

Imagine you have to make some of the things you need from natural materials. These might be

a shelter . a cooking tool . a piece of clothing . a musical instrument.

Choose a big item (e.g. a shelter or a boat) to make a model of, or a smaller item (e.g. a cooking tool or a musical instrument) to make. Draw up a design and try making your item using natural materials as much as you can.

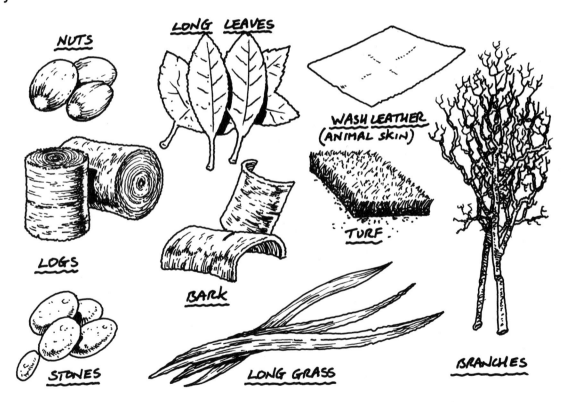

If your design needs clay from the earth, you could use modelling clay.
For animal gut you could use elastic or fishing line.
For animal skin, you could use wash leather.

Being there

Some environmental problems seem a long way off, but children can go on a drama expedition to the places affected.

The link between human activity and the well-being of the planet is now one of the most important reasons for learning about the environment. However, many environmental problems occur in places which are distant and seem beyond the reach of our own experience. The aim of this project is to enable a class to 'pack up and leave' their home area and, by using some of the simple techniques of drama work, to develop a sense of 'being there'.

■ TRIP TO A THREATENED FOREST

A piece of wood, a few grains of rice or an exotic fruit may be the stimulus for an investigation into the effects of deforestation in a tropical area like the Brazilian Amazon. Such objects, possibly already familiar to the children, can give a clue to the scenery and the economic life of the country. Information from books or from the teacher can be used to follow this up. However, Juan's letter (below) can be used as a more personal, alternative opening to adventure. I leave it to readers' own ingenuity to give Juan a character and a situation. Again, teachers could choose to provide clues - raw materials, artefacts, clippings from newspapers, drawings, other letters - for a class to use to piece together the threads of Juan's life and the implications of this distressing letter.

A group or class planning session should be used to enable all the children to have their say about the direction and content of the project. Once everyone has agreed that it will be necessary to have an expedition to study the area and see what aspects of it are under threat, the children must decide what their individual duties on the expedition will be:
- ❏ studying plants
- ❏ studying animals
- ❏ arranging transport
- ❏ looking after food.

The teacher also needs to decide what role she or he will take in the project. The role of guide to the expedition is a good one from which to help with the direction of the drama.

Using maps and reference books, the children should research their proposed areas of study and prepare a plan of what they will do at each stage along the route. Filling in a planning sheet like the one on page 47 can lead on to drawing up a route-plan. Equipment lists must be drawn up (stock lists obtained from science equipment and outdoor pursuits equipment suppliers will help here), but the children should remember that they can only take what they can carry. Some ruthless decisions may have to be taken about what is 'necessary' and what must be left behind.

The next stage is to select a location on the way to the rainforest to act as a

---

'The Village in the Forest'

Dear Friends

As I write, the rain is pattering down on the leaves above my head. It rains most days, but not for long. When it stops, the silence and the heat sometimes seem impossible to bear.

But today is different. Today, for the first time in this part of the forest, I heard men laughing and machines roaring. I could also hear the sound of my beloved trees crashing to the ground. The silence has gone.

All seems lost. I fear this letter will be my last from this place.

Your friend

Juan

focus for ideas or experiences. I have found the airport particularly useful for this purpose because it represents a point of departure in the mind as well as the body.

The expedition members arrive at the airport and struggle with their bags to the departure lounge. Here, they may form small groups and chat together, or choose to sit alone. Each member of the group is given the opportunity to consider her or his situation.

❏   Are they leaving loved ones behind?
❏   Is there danger ahead?
❏   What will it be like in the forest?

Ask some of the children to speak their thoughts aloud (this is called **thought tracking**).

■ SETTING OFF ON THE TREK

Once you have developed a feel for the group and the situations they are expecting to find themselves in, it is a simple matter to develop the story, adding additional business as you go along. For example, you may wish to start the expedition proper in a small town in Brazil. Some of the group could attempt to order food and supplies from a store in the town. They might even learn a few useful words of Portuguese. Is there someone who speaks this language who could play the role of the village store-keeper?

During the long and difficult trek through the forest, the members of the expedition will be studying a variety of plants and animals. This part of the project can be developed using books, slides and even films. Perhaps someone who has visited a rainforest could be persuaded to come and talk to your class. A visit to a zoo or butterfly house could provide information about the animals and plants that live in a rainforest. You could even use this opportunity to look at minibeasts that live in the school grounds, trying out some of the scientific equipment you have decided to take. Work previously done by the class on unusual plants (for example, the children may have tried growing their own exotic fruit from pineapple crowns, avocado stones etc. - see p.48) could be brought in too. In a cross-curricular project, the expedition members could combine science and technology, and could design and build their own shelter, making tents or other structures that use the natural materials they would find about them.

■ OVERCOMING PROBLEMS

What difficulties might the children encounter when camping in the jungle? Let the children suggest some. Obvious ones are:

❏   the presence of biting insects
❏   the accumulation of fatigue
❏   the lack of proper medical supplies.

All of these could affect whether the expedition keeps on going or has to turn back.

Other hardships and challenges to be faced on the trek through the rainforest might include:

- ❏ forcing a path through thick undergrowth
- ❏ sheltering from a sudden storm
- ❏ crossing an old rope bridge
- ❏ a tree falling across the path
- ❏ the presence of a dangerous animal nearby.

Such events can be built into a very effective series of mini-dramas. If there is time to provide a forest background to these, building one makes an enjoyable technology task. A diagram to help build the scenery is given on page 48.

Allow the children to form smaller groups, and give each group one of the above situations. Their task is to develop a short piece of drama to show what happened and how the characters reacted to the events described. Avoid the use of props; and in these dramas ask the actors only to portray people, not animals or trees.

When ready, the class can become observers and watch each group's work separately. At certain places in the drama, 'freeze' the participants and ask them to speak their thoughts aloud. **Freeze framing** is a wonderful way of focusing attention on situations, and I have used the technique many times to examine how children have felt in difficult or unusual circumstances.

■ VITAL RESOURCES

Rainforests are very productive places: the ingredients for many common products, including aftershave, lipstick and coffee, have their origin there. One quarter of all our medicine is derived from rainforest plants, and many more useful plants may be waiting to be discovered.

Consider how different groups of people use the rainforest, the materials they obtain from it, and the effects they have on it.

- ❏ Loggers cut down trees and this provides timber, but they are destroying the forest ecosystem.
- ❏ Rubber tappers, on the other hand, remove only small quantities of latex from individual trees, without harming the forest.

Now is the moment to bring in the people who live in the forest. A brainstorming session can produce an outline of the sort of 'occupations' that the villagers have. Some of the children might even become villagers and act out scenes from their lives. Use freeze framing and thought tracking to demonstrate different jobs within the village. How important is the forest to the people who live there?

Deforestation is the single greatest threat to the livelihood of hundreds of thousands of forest people, and the direct cause of plant and animal extinctions on a massive scale. To understand deforestation, the children need to become a part of it.

Let the children become forest trees, the 'protectors' of all other plants and animals. See what kinds of shapes and patterns they make with their bodies. Let them reach towards the sky and feel the warmth of the sun on their leaves, feel the wind drifting slowly through their branches and the rain cooling their tall, thick trunks. The earth seems to pull at their roots and force life into them. Then, with slow, deliberate actions, 'cut' the trees down. Thought track the children and hear how they feel about being cut down.

Pictures and video films help to convey the full significance of deforestation. Paintings, posters and poetry can then be used to describe the desolation that follows the destruction of a rainforest.

■ QUESTIONS THAT MUST BE ASKED

The study will raise many questions:
- ❑ Why are the forests being cut down?
- ❑ What happens to the plants and animals?
- ❑ Where will the villagers get their food and water from?
- ❑ What will happen to the rubber tappers?
- ❑ How does deforestation in one area affect people living in other parts of the world?
- ❑ How can we save the forests?

There are other simple techniques which may be used to develop your study:
- ❑ **Narration** can be used to pass on information, mark the passing of time and create atmosphere.
- ❑ **Sound tracking** can provide realistic noises to enhance the sense of place.
- ❑ Various **interviewing techniques** can help focus attention on ideas or how people feel about an event.
- ❑ **Letters** can be sent back from the jungle, along with photographs of important events in the expedition's travels.

This type of simulation can be developed to suit any age group or ability range, and elements of it can be removed and used independently.

Drama is a great motivator. It transcends subject barriers and brings with it a sense of involvement that is difficult to generate second-hand. Issues, no less important for occurring in far-off places, can be brought directly into the classroom. In the words of Dorothy Heathcote, 'Let's pack up and leave . . . I talk like I'm already there'.

Subject checklist

Science: studying the plants and animals of the tropical rainforests; the properties and uses of natural materials.

Technology: designing and building shelters; designing and building a tropical rainforest scene.

Geography: studying conditions in a tropical rainforest; products of the rainforest; occupations of rainforest people.

English: narrating a story; writing letters.

Books
Conserving Rainforests (**Conserving Our World** series) Wayland 1991, ISBN 1 85210 695 6.
Disappearing Rainforest Robert Prosser (**Considering Conservation** series) Dryad 1987, ISBN 0 8521 9719 5.
Rainforests (**Tell Me About Nature** series) Kingfisher 1991, ISBN 0 8627 2728 6.
Rainforest Fiona Macdonald (**New View** series) Franklin Watts 1992, ISBN 0 7496 0657 6.
Rainforests Brian Knapp (**Caring for Environments** series) Simon & Schuster 1991, ISBN 0 7500 0861 X.

Chart
Pictorial Charts Educational Trust, 27 Kirchen Road, London W13 OUD produces *Tropical Rainforests* (T69).

Useful address
Vesutor Ltd, Bromeliad Nursery, Marringdean Road, Billingshurst, West Sussex RH14 9EH supply a range of tropical fruit seedlings for use in schools.

EXPEDITION PLANNING SHEET

TASKS	STUDYING PLANTS	STUDYING ANIMALS	TRANSPORT	FOOD AND SHELTER
Expedition members				
To find out before setting off				
Sources of information				
Need to do before setting off				
Need to take on expedition				
Most important tasks during expedition				

GROWING TROPICAL PLANTS

AVOCADO 'STONE'

MATCHSTICKS

WATER

PINCH BACK

POT

SOIL

①

②

DO-IT-YOURSELF TROPICAL RAINFOREST

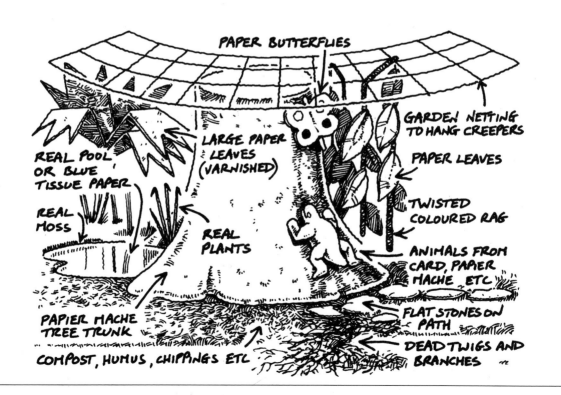

PAPER BUTTERFLIES

GARDEN NETTING TO HANG CREEPERS

PAPER LEAVES

LARGE PAPER LEAVES (VARNISHED)

REAL POOL OR BLUE TISSUE PAPER

TWISTED COLOURED RAG

REAL MOSS

REAL PLANTS

ANIMALS FROM CARD, PAPER MACHE ETC

PAPIER MACHE TREE TRUNK

FLAT STONES ON PATH

DEAD TWIGS AND BRANCHES

COMPOST, HUMUS, CHIPPINGS ETC

Section 3

Is life getting healthier?

Yesterday's children

Most young children today are surprised to be told that 150 years ago they would not have been at school, but would already have been working. The members of Learning Through Action, a group of teachers based in Berkshire, devised the following programme to introduce children to nineteenth-century working England through role play and research. Designed for upper junior and middle school children, 'Yesterday's Children' lasts for two hours when run by the Learning Through Action team of four teachers; but it can easily be adapted to be run by a group of teachers in their school hall or even in their own classrooms and over a time period that suits them.

■ GETTING DOWN TO WORK

The programme begins with one member of the teacher team talking to the class about historical research and the sources that can be used - reports, letters, diaries, pictures and artefacts. The use of role play to help participants empathise with people in the past is also discussed.

In their first activity, all the children are enrolled as workhouse paupers and put on ragged shirts. Together with a teacher, they explore life in the workhouse, picking oakum (unravelling old rope to get the fibres - a common workhouse activity) and inspecting the sort of bones that would have been used to make the workhouse inmates' staple diet of gruel.

The children are then split into four groups and sent off by the workhouse as child labour for employers, just as they would have been in the nineteenth century. The four working groups each look at one industry:
❑ matchmaking
❑ mining
❑ textile manufacture
❑ farming.

The technology and working conditions of the past come under scrutiny as children take on the roles of child labourers in Victorian England.

Working in small groups is a key element in the 'Yesterday's Children' project. Each group should be run by a teacher or adult helper in role as a worker, dressed in a rough attempt at nineteenth-century clothes. The worker tells stories about her or his life in the workplace, showing the children some of the tools of the job and describing the ways in which they were used.

The worker's narrative should not be a passive listening session: children should be actively involved, asking questions of the worker and assimilating more information than they might from a book because of the personal, storytelling element.

■ EVERYDAY STRUGGLES

The teacher may give a general description of the industry she or he is representing before dealing with the child labour element in it. Or she or he may choose to focus from the beginning on the life of a child labourer. For example, a teacher in role as a worker in the **mines** can concentrate on the daily routine of a child mineworker. From this angle, which should have a special meaning for them, the children can consider topics such as the dangers of working in a coal mine, the machinery, the hours, the wages and other social and economic factors.

The teacher can show pictures of mines from books and packs that the school has in stock or has borrowed. If it can be arranged, it is also a good idea to offer samples of coal, and perhaps to demonstrate a 'Davy' miner's lamp and one of the axes used to hack at the coal face. An 'eyewitness' account of a mining disaster such as an explosion or a flood can be put together by a teacher from reference material, and this serves as a harrowing reminder of the dangers of the industry.

The **match factory** group can have a go themselves at making match-boxes from pieces of card and glue, and see how nimble-fingered they would have to be to make enough each day. The teacher in role as worker can instruct them in their efforts as well as telling tales of the long hours, the unhealthy buildings and the poisonous phosphorus which was used in matchmaking and resulted in so many workers suffering from 'phossy jaw', the slow rotting of the jawbone.

The **textile mill** children can learn something of the mechanisation of spinning and weaving, and of the terrible accidents that occurred as tired children scrambled about underneath machines that were introduced without any idea of having safety guards.

For the **farmwork** group, the physical effort needed from people and animals to power machinery such as ploughs can be evoked, and the constant struggle with the weather and pests. For older children, comparisons can be made with other sorts of work - for example with mining, which required more concentration and skill and offered more danger, but paid better wages.

The children should be in their groups for about half an hour before the teacher 'de-roles'. The workplace technology and the conditions of the working children are then discussed from a present-day point of view, with questions answered and comparisons made with modern times.

Children are then introduced to a research activity where they are asked to investigate more thoroughly some of the topics that have come up in their group discussions.

■ FURTHER INVESTIGATIONS

The individual groups 'brainstorm' areas they might like to research, and discussion of these areas throws up questions to which the group members must find answers.

Some children may decide to find out more about the technical side of the work. What were the benefits for production, and the dangers for the workers, of the machinery used in a particular industry?

Others may wish to research how workers lived - their food, housing and working conditions.

Other topics could include the inventors of the technology, or the employers, or the social reformers who struggled for safer working conditions.

At this point, the children are offered a variety of resources to help with research.

❏ Role bank
This is a table with a collection of items of clothing and names of characters which go with the clothes. Children ask to interview one of the suggested characters, and a teacher puts on an appropriate item of clothing, takes on the role of that character and answers the children's questions.

A role table can be created easily in the classroom by collecting hats, scarves, aprons etc to indicate characters such as the mother of a child worker, the foreman of a cotton mill or a reformer like Lord Shaftesbury. As well as being researched and taken on by the teacher, roles may also be researched by children (this applies to children at the top end of the age range) and taken on by them to assist each other.

Interviewing a variety of people helps the children to get a balanced view of an event or period and assess the reliability and the authenticity of various sources.

❏ Computer
The use of information technology can enhance the research element of a research and drama programme like 'Yesterday's Children', and a 'Touch Explorer Plus' package has been devised by Learning Through Action to provide children with information at several levels of difficulty. This package is used with a concept keyboard to create an information retrieval program which children can use to access and print information

about their particular industry. The information was researched and selected from various sources by the LTA team, but teachers could assemble their own information and sort it into levels of difficulty before putting it on computer.

❑ **Artefacts**

Assuming roles as owners or users of artefacts increases children's interest and concentration. The learning comes alive, and new areas of enquiry open up. For example, a man-trap can be used to enhance the storytelling for the farmwork group and stimulate such questions as:
Who set man-traps and why?
Why did so many people living in the countryside need to poach?

Collecting simple artefacts is not difficult. They may be gathered from a variety of sources, from junk shops to 'granny's attic'. Some organisations, such as local or industrial museums, may be willing to lend out such artefacts as lamps or worktools, or in the case of more delicate items to lend out copies. As a classroom activity, children can make their own versions of such artefacts as matchboxes, birdscarers and threshing flails, which they can then use in role.

❑ **Information packs**

A collection of pictures and articles selected by teachers from books and packs on Victorian machinery, industry, work, housing, clothes, food and health can act as a stimulus for the children to begin their own research.

■ PUTTING IT ALL TOGETHER

During the research session, children are encouraged to work as if they were either contemporary historians or Victorian journalists and to gather material they could use for a case study of a Victorian working child, written from one of these two points of view.

At the end of their research, the groups gather in a forum session with their notebooks to share and discuss their findings. Following this, the pieces of writing by historians or journalists can be produced.

As well as making their findings available to others verbally, children often bring to the forum session a selection of artefacts, or drawings of artefacts, from the programme. In demonstrating the use of these to back up their words, they are taking their cue from the practical nature of the whole session and helping to create a picture of 'yesterday's children'.

Subject checklist
Science: understanding forces and energy in the context of industry; the properties of industrial raw materials; nutritional needs.
Technology: studying the design of machines.
Information technology: using information packages for research.
History: understanding social conditions in Victorian Britain; social reformers.
Geography: finding out where Victorian industries developed and why.

Books
Factory (**Through the Ages** series) Eagle Books 1990, ISBN 1 8551 1071 7.
Revolution and Technology Ann Kramer and Simon Adams (**Historical Atlases** series) Kingfisher 1991, ISBN 0 8627 2759 6.
Victorians: Early & Late David Evans (**How We Used to Live** series) A & C Black 1990, ISBN 0 7136 3310 7.
Victorian Times Paul Noble and Jo Lawrie Collins 1991, ISBN 0 0444 8126 8.

Pack
Learning Through Action, Cumberland Road, Reading RG1 3JY produces a 'Yesterday's Children' pack of photocopiable materials.

Software
Acorn Computers Ltd, Fulbourn Road, Cambridge CB1 4JN supplies *Victorian Britain*. Suitable for Acorn/Archimedes.

Epidemic

Standpipe in Bethnal Green, London, 1863.

Pupils take a dramatic step into the nineteenth century to learn about the factors that affect public health.

The project described here is one I devised after I had been on a drama course for teachers. After learning about warming up, mime and voice exercises, we went on to role-play. Being a great cribber of ideas for science, I decided this was just the thing for a different sort of science lesson. I could help my pupils (top juniors) absorb some key science ideas; and I could also foster group work and communication amongst them, developing ways of reporting, responding and communicating, as the National Curriculum had told me to do.

■ HEALTH EDUCATION

I brought my new enthusiasm for drama to bear on a subject I wanted to make my pupils more aware of: health education. And I soon found that from a very simple skeleton lesson I was able to build up an exercise and an experience in which pupils became totally absorbed.

My exercise was based, very loosely, on what I was able to read about the global cholera pandemic of 1817 to 1823. I began by pretending to be King William IV opening Parliament in 1831, though I used only his opening words, 'It is with deep concern that I have to announce to you the continued progress of a formidable disease in Eastern Europe . . .' After that, I made up his speech, in role, not dwelling on political events, but concentrating on the reasons for the spread of disease in that period (before Pasteur developed vaccination):

❑   poor food
❑   poor air
❑   poor water
❑   the general disorganised living conditions of the poor.

For this **first session**, I divided the class into small groups who took on the roles of characters of the period to discuss the spread of the disease. We then listened in turn to each group as its members discussed the spread of disease.

The children had chosen to portray a wide range of types, from learned scientists to 'Smith and Jones' bar flies. We finished off the first stage of the exercise by writing shock-horror newspaper reports of cholera raging across Europe. Writing and reading these helped the children to understand the importance of getting the scientific facts right in newspapers, and how the slanting of articles could make them more or less helpful to anxious readers.

■ 19TH-CENTURY LIVING CONDITIONS

In our **second session**, I felt it was important to build up the role-play by exploring the condition of many of the poor. We used the following small piece, written in the first half of the nineteenth century about the poor in Leeds, as a starting point:

'By far the most unhealthy localities of Leeds are close squares of houses, or yards as they are called, which have been erected for the accommodation of working people. Some of these, though situated in comparatively high ground, are airless from the enclosed structure and being wholly unprovided with any form of drainage, or convenience (privy) or arrangements for washing.

They are one mass of damp and filth.

The ashes and garbage, and filth of all kinds are thrown from the doors and windows of the houses upon the surface of streets and courts. The privies are few for the number of inhabitants and are open to view in front and rear. They are invariably in a filthy condition and often remain without the removal of filth for six months.'

The children came to empathise with poor factory workers by acting out, in groups, imaginary scenes from these people's domestic lives. These scenes also increased the immediacy of the health problems in the minds of the children.

■ ARE THE PIES TO BLAME?

The **third session** opened with the class being divided into groups once more. Each group consisted of
- ❑   three doctors
- ❑   a pie-shop owner
- ❑   a representative of the Town Council
- ❑   a clergyman working among the poor of the town.

Each group was given an envelope which I had prepared. In it was the following information:

It is a hot summer in . . . . town. The town is a large mill town, with many poor workers whose homes are cheap dwellings, built quickly. Two weeks ago, the keeper of the town's most popular shop was brought before the magistrates for selling pies containing putrid meat. The shopkeeper protested that he kept his shop clean but the heat had caused the pies to go off quickly. He was fined.

Each group received information specifically for one of their number, a Dr Woodley:

> Dr Woodley has accompanied the Vicar of St Mary's, Cottage Hill, to treat two girls who have fallen ill with a serious stomach complaint.
> Dr Woodley has been told that the girls stopped at a pie shop for a snack when going to visit their grandmother in Mill Street.

The pupil playing Dr Woodley had to report the information to the rest of the group. While he was reporting, the pupil chosen as the pie-shop owner received an envelope.

> The owner of the pie shop where the two girls stopped for a snack is a small tradesman. If he is closed down, he will lose his home and business. However, he has a friend who is a councillor, whom he will ask to help him in the discussion.
> The pie-shop owner claims he has been in business for fifteen years, has been a reliable small tradesman, and has had no complaints.

■ WATER AND SANITATION

Groups were given maps (see page 58) of the fictitious town, but without the water pumps or privies marked. This information was available on an overlay for the map (see page 60) which I kept to myself.

If you examine the map on page 58 together with the overlay, you will see that the infection is spreading along the eastern streets, and that privies and pumps are close. The underground streams were also not on the street map given out to the children; but when added, they showed there was a likelihood that material from the privies was entering the drinking water.

The idea that lack of cleanliness at the pie shop was spreading the disease was a deliberate piece of irrelevance, designed to draw attention from the cluster of cases in the east.

The groups were asked to study the maps, think about the reasons why the disease might be spreading, and draw up a plan to try to halt it. As they worked, I fed in information about new cases which had broken out, using the map shown on page 59.

During the **fourth session**, the groups swapped their plans and each group discussed what its members considered were the good and bad points of the plan that had been passed to them. Moving between groups, I dropped various facts into the discussions - pointing out, for example, that people in those days did not have money for lots of fuel to boil quantities of water, that they had no means of transporting a lot of water, and that there were no isolation hospitals.

I then challenged the groups to reconsider their solutions to the problem, suggesting what public health improvements needed to be made in the community. Many sensible ideas emerged, but there was also an awareness of what must have frustrated the doctors, clergy and town councils at the time, a sense that the improvements suggested were for the future, and for the moment the only thing the characters could do was to bury the dead and weep.

■ SCIENCE AND EMOTION

What I found of most benefit as a science teacher was the acute emotional involvement of my pupils in the struggle against disease. Although I used the term 'taken ill' for victims, groups seemed to assume that death would follow, and a real sense of urgency took over. Perhaps that is what we miss in some school science - a sense that it is not just a dry academic exercise, but that the knowledge and understanding we are gaining affect people's lives. Indeed, as I fed information into the groups, the doctors would ask 'Is the girl at Number 27 The Butts any better? Have I cured her?' I would answer 'Not yet', and worried frowns followed.

The basic 'scientific drama' obviously has other possibilities. Because the nineteenth-century setting was limiting in that we could not cure victims or bring about anachronistic public health improvements during the course of the drama, I have toyed with the idea of setting a future health drama in a refugee camp, or after an earthquake, where measures that we are now all familiar with could be taken quickly.

I also want to look again at the action plans the children developed. Why did pupils almost always suggest tidying up the streets and stopping people indiscriminately throwing out garbage, rather than suggest they wash their hands and boil their drinking water? Was this due to the way I had introduced the project, or did my pupils, even in this scientific age, not have enough experience of the various forms prevention of disease takes?

I must warn you, setting up role-play is a very noisy experience. Some children weep and become very over-stressed because of their roles. Attacks made on the shopkeeper in one group led to a genuinely distressing experience for the boy playing him, who was unable to separate himself from the character. Time does need to be allowed to get in and out of role, and there are dangers in letting yourself become too involved and letting things run on. However, role-play is exciting for teacher and class, and offers a very different sort of science lesson, one that I want to refine and repeat.

Subject checklist
Science: learning about the spread of germs and disease, and how these can be prevented.
Technology: studying the layout of nineteenth-century towns.
History: looking at town life in the nineteenth century.
Geography: understanding patterns of settlement and industrial growth.
English: writing reports; assessing other people's arguments.

Books
Germs Make Me Sick Melvin Berger (**First Sight** series) A & C Black 1989, ISBN 0 7136 3092 2.
Finding out about Industrial Britain Madeline Jones Batsford 1984, ISBN 0 7134 4353 7.
Life in Victorian Britain Fiona Goodman and Peter Kent (**Investigating History** series) Simon & Schuster 1992, ISBN 0 7500 0215 2.
Living Long Ago: Homes and Houses Helen Edom (**Explainers** series) Usborne 1989, ISBN 0 7460 0450 8.
Towns and Cities of the Past Laurie Bolwell and Cliff Lines (**Towns and Cities** series) Wayland 1985, ISBN 0 85078 704 1.

MAP OF THE TOWN

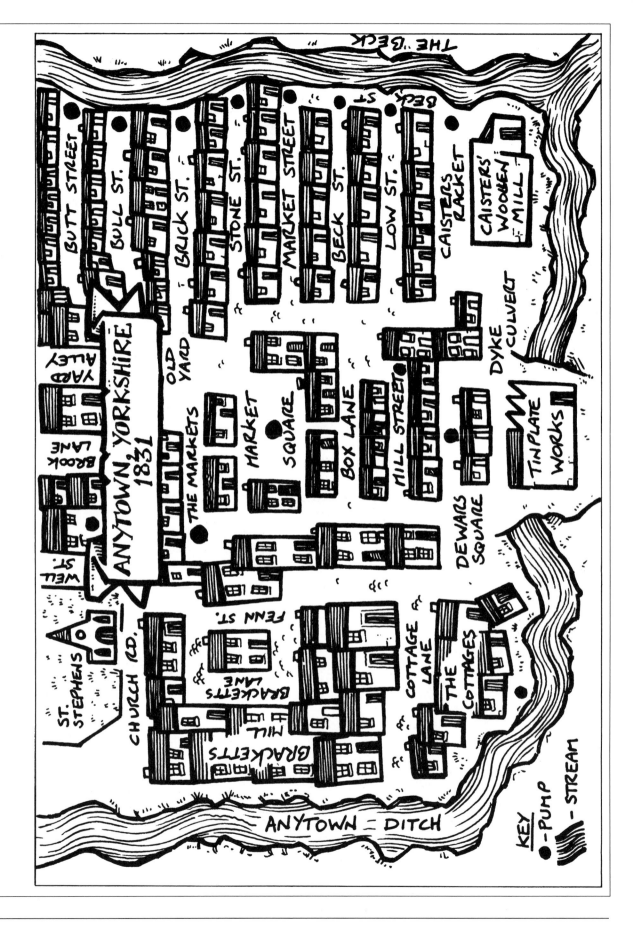

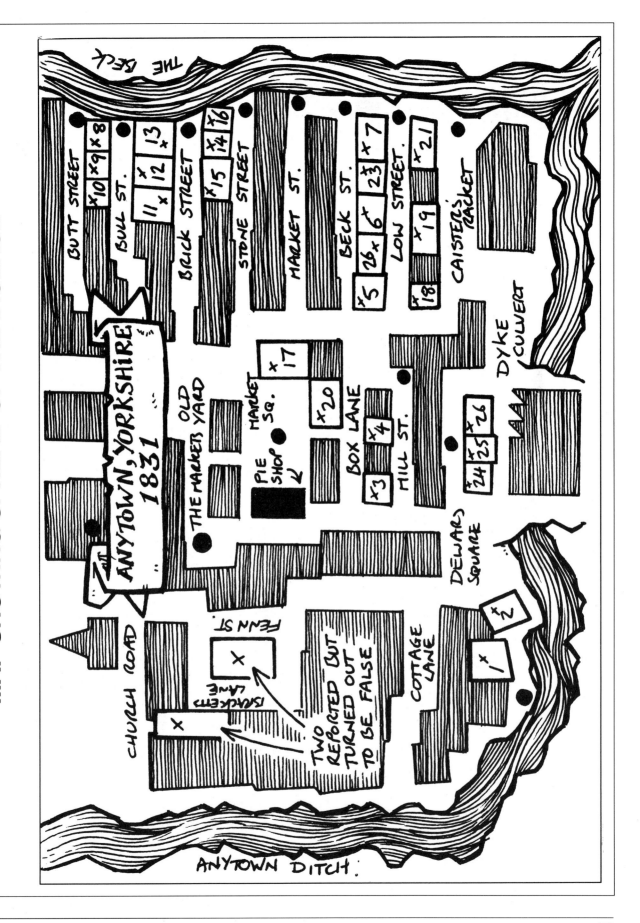

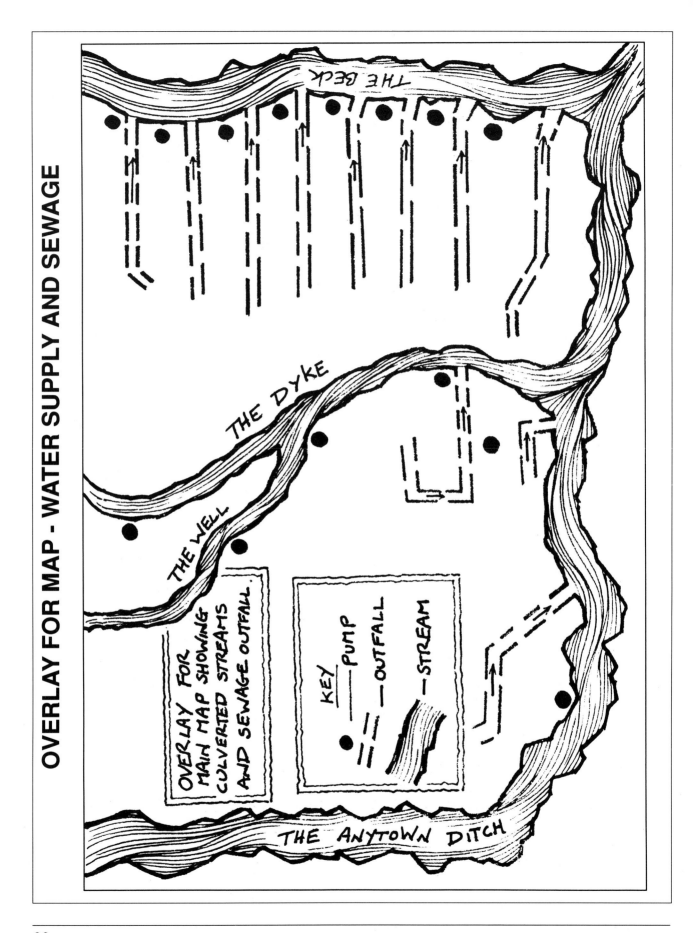

OVERLAY FOR MAP - WATER SUPPLY AND SEWAGE

THE BECK

THE DYKE

THE WELL

THE ANYTOWN DITCH

OVERLAY FOR MAIN MAP SHOWING CULVERTED STREAMS AND SEWAGE OUTFALL.

KEY

— PUMP

— — OUTFALL

— STREAM

●

FACTFILE: GERMS AND INFECTION

Infectious diseases are caused by **pathogenic microorganisms**, i.e. parasitic organisms, too small to see with the naked eye, which damage body tissues. When these organisms invade the body and start to multiply in great numbers, the host is said to be **infected**. The symptoms of infection vary widely, but a very common symptom is **fever**: an increase in body temperature caused by the body's attempt to overcome the infection.

Germ transmission can take several routes:

- in water droplets (from sneezing/coughing) in the air
- in contaminated water
- in contaminated food
- by physical contact, either direct or indirect (clothes, blankets etc)
- in blood via blood transfusions, donor organs etc
- by a living carrier e.g. rats, mosquitoes, fleas.

Some forms of germ are unable to survive without a living carrier or **host**; most cannot survive hostile conditions (heat, detergents etc) outside the body. The body's own defences against infectious disease are of two kinds:

1. **Non-specific**: fever, inflammation, fluid secretions (to wash away germs), action of **white blood cells** which attack and engulf germs.

2. **Specific**: humans have an **immune response** to pathogenic elements, producing specific **antibodies** which circulate in the bloodstream and can kill or inactivate germs.

Types of disease agent

1. BACTERIA

These are simple single-celled organisms. Diseases caused by bacterial infection include:

- **tuberculosis** - this is caused by **tubercle bacilli**, which infect the lung tissue.
- **food poisoning** - this is usually caused by *Salmonella* bacteria, which multiply rapidly in warm food.
- **cholera** - this bacterial species only infects humans. It is spread by water or (more rarely) food contaminated by human excrement. The major symptom is diarrhoea, leading to dehydration and circulatory failure.

2. VIRUSES

These are the smallest known living particles. When it comes into contact with a living cell, a virus injects its **nuclear material** into the host cell, which is forced to produce new virus particles.

Diseases caused by viral infection include:

- **chickenpox** - spread primarily by coughing, but the visible skin lesions are also infectious.
- **smallpox** - similar to chickenpox, but the symptoms are far more dangerous. Smallpox has now been eradicated by the use of vaccination and quarantine.
- **poliomyelitis** - this is spread by food or water contaminated with human faeces; the virus infects the brain and nervous system, causing paralysis.
- **influenza** - the major strain of this virus causes winter epidemics, and is liable to periodic changes.

3. FUNGI

The most common fungal infections of the human body are caused by the genus *Tinea*, and are commonly known as **ringworm** (because infections spread in rings on the skin).

4. PROTOZOA

These are single-celled organisms, larger and more advanced than bacteria. Diseases caused by protozoa include:

■ **dysentery** - this is caused by an amoeba which **encysts** in food or water and invades the human gut wall.

■ **malaria** - this is caused by the *Plasmodium* amoeba, which is carried by the *Anopheles* mosquito. It multiplies in the human liver and red blood cells.

5. WORMS

Parasitic worms which invade the human body are ingested in the form of eggs or **encysted larvae** in food. Examples include the **beef tapeworm** and the more primitive **threadworm**, which is spread by poor hygiene.

Prevention and cure

There are several ways of fighting infectious diseases:

1. **Hygiene** - the single most important **preventive** measure. It includes:

■ washing hands before eating or drinking and after using the toilet

■ keeping the body clean and dry

■ keeping food clean, fresh and away from insects

■ purification of water supplies; boiling of potentially unsafe water before use

■ covering of wounds; treatment of wounds with **antiseptic** (germ-killing) substances; surgery under antiseptic conditions.

2. **Quarantine**: the isolation of contagious individuals.

3. **Medicine**. Various treatments can help the infected patient, either by alleviating the symptoms or by killing the disease germ. **Antibiotics** are chemical preparations which kill pathogenic bacteria or inhibit their growth; a famous example is **penicillin**. Viruses can very rarely be cured in this way.

4. **Food preparation**: freezing, refrigeration, sterilisation and pasteurisation of food and drinks.

5. **Immunisation**. There are two ways of conferring immunity against an infection. **Passive immunity** can be conferred by injecting specific antibodies derived from an immune person. **Active immunity** can be conferred by **vaccination**, which uses a weakened form of the disease (called a **vaccine**) to stimulate the patient's **own** immune response.

Dramatic discoveries

Learning about aspects of medicine combines with research into some remarkable lives when children take on the roles of pioneering medical scientists.

The lives of famous scientists offer a rich range of possibilities for combining science and drama. In the following suggestions for drama work, the field is narrowed to that of medical science, and the suggestions are centred on the lives of two scientists in particular. However, similar strategies could be used to explore other famous lives.

■ ENTERING A DRAMA

The space is set out as a doctor's waiting room with rows of chairs and a receptionist's desk. Here the children (upper juniors) can bring in their own experiences of going to the doctor or to the hospital 'out-patients'.

The receptionist asks the children to sit in two sections - medical and surgical. This should stimulate discussion about the differences between the two and this discussion can be developed when the teacher, in role as the doctor, enters and questions the patients to check whether they are in the right section.

The teacher - or the class as a whole - chooses one of the patients who is likely to be having an operation. The class then splits into two groups:
one concerned with the 1990s
one concerned with the 1860s.

Operation at Charing Cross Hospital, c1900.

Each group does some research to build up a scene showing an operation in their period. When the groups are ready, some of the members of each make a still picture of their operation. Then the children, both those watching and those taking part in the still pictures, become involved in comparing and contrasting the two types of scene. Some ways of doing this are:

❑ The teacher asks the participants in the scenes about their role and they answer in role.

❑ Children in one of the research groups (but not in their group's scene) enter, introduce people in the scene and comment on their role.

❑ Some children are kept back as observers to report to the whole class on the differences and similarities that they can identify.

■ LINKS WITH THE PAST

To give the operations more personal interest for the children, select two groups of children and ask one to create a family from the 1990s and the other to create a family from the 1860s. Each family has a member undergoing a serious operation, and each is given specific information and instructions linked to their family's circumstances, for example:

> The person undergoing the operation is the 'breadwinner' of the family. Your group should consider how the other members of the family would be affected if anything should happen to him/her. Relatives should speak in role about how they would be affected.

Ask the class which patient is more likely to survive. What makes the difference? Some main differences are:

knowledge about **germs**

the existence of **antiseptics**

the possibility of **blood transfusions**

the existence of **anaesthetics**

the existence of **monitoring machines** and other technology.

The preliminary work already described sets the context for what follows. Let us consider two aspects of the above list of differences between the 1990s and the 1860s: antiseptics, which brings in Joseph Lister; and the storage of blood for re-use, which brings in Charles Drew.

■ JOSEPH LISTER

Lister's is a familiar name. His main contribution to medicine was in the pioneering of antiseptics.

Working as a surgeon in Scotland, Lister read about Louis Pasteur's work on microbes in France. He related his failure to keep some patients alive during operations to Pasteur's discoveries about germs, and decided to experiment with killing germs in the operating theatre. He tried using carbolic acid on wounds; and this, although it caused great discomfort, prevented infection setting in. Later, Lister developed a milder but equally effective antiseptic. He also tried to sterilise the whole room by spraying

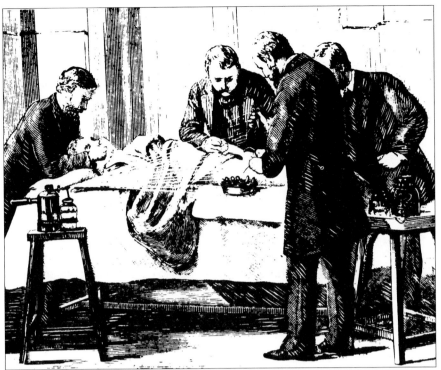

Operation using Lister's spray.

antiseptic into the air - a practice which caused problems for the theatre staff as well as the germs.

Lister extended his work, developing:

boracic acid-impregnated lint dressings

the heat sterilisation of surgical instruments

the wearing of special garments by theatre staff.

Strategies for considering Joseph Lister's life and work could include:

❏ Meet Lister. See him at his desk. Children sitting around him speak his thoughts as he struggles with the problems he had - patients dying of infection and wounds failing to heal. Whoever takes the Lister role here could dress appropriately. A laboratory work bench could be set up to help focus attention.

❏ Introduce Lister to Pasteur. Although Lister only read about Pasteur's work, dramatic licence could be used to bring the two together. Here, the class could work in pairs, as Pasteur explains his work and Lister questions him. Research into Pasteur's life will be needed for this, of course.

❏ Meet Lister as if he and the class were contemporaries in the medical field. This could be done in several contexts:

Lister lectures to medical students.

Lister meets other surgeons who are sceptical about his ideas. In particular, Simpson, who was a pioneer of anaesthetics, opposed Lister's ideas. Here, the teacher could take the role of Lister to give the children a chance to ask questions.

❏ The children create scenes in which they are in the operating theatre with Lister. Research will again be needed to make it authentic: for example, spraying the air with antiseptic and reacting to this, scrubbing up and preparing instruments will all be important.

■ DR CHARLES DREW

Charles Drew is much less well known than Joseph Lister. Drew's main contribution to medicine was discovering the method of separating plasma from blood, so that blood could be stored for emergency use. An American, Drew came to Britain in 1939 and established blood banks, becoming Medical Director of the British Blood Transfusion Association.

Some of the strategies suggested for considering the life and work of Joseph Lister could be used with Charles Drew:

❏ Operation scenes before and after the introduction of blood transfusion could be set up.

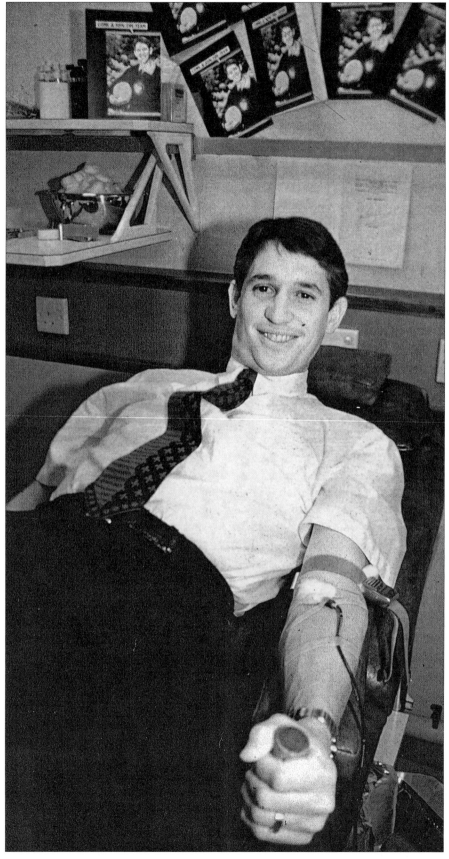

Stars like footballer Gary Lineker lend their support to campaigns for blood donors.

❑ Children in role as medical students or fellow doctors could question Drew about his discovery.

For such activities, research will be needed into the composition of blood and into blood circulation in the human body.

In 1950, Drew was badly injured in a car crash in the United States and was rushed to the nearest hospital. At the hospital, however, he was refused the treatment he needed, including a blood transfusion, and had to go to another hospital. He died before he could reach the second hospital.

Why was Drew refused treatment at the first hospital?

Because this was North Carolina (one of the southern states), the hospital was 'whites only' and Charles Drew was black.

This very sad story could offer children the opportunity to set advances in medical science against their social background:

❑ Pupils could improvise the scene where Drew is taken to the first hospital and turned away.

❑ Pupils not in the scene could observe a specific participant and note what he or she did or said in the scene - arguments or even non-verbal signs which related to the principle of refusing treatment. These could be written out on large posters. At the funeral or memorial service, these observations could be displayed or spoken as a dramatic piece of theatre.

❑ People from Britain whose lives have been saved by Drew's work could also attend and contribute an opinion or express their feelings about those who had turned him away.

■ WIDENING THE EXPERIENCE

These are only two contributors to medical science. Children could be encouraged to develop their research to look at a variety of scientists and their work:

Harvey - the circulation of blood

Pasteur - work on microbial life

Jenner - inoculation of the smallpox vaccine

Kolff - a Dutch doctor who also worked to establish blood banks, and who invented the artificial kidney machine in Occupied Holland during World War II.

The following suggestions are ways of bringing in first-hand experience that is outside the drama but related to it:

❑ Meet a real hospital doctor or nurse to talk about their work. If the children know that they are going to recreate hospitals and operating theatres in drama work, their questioning will be more purposeful.

❑ Use museum services to obtain real surgical tools of the period, as a way of creating atmosphere and focusing attention.

❑ Use microscopes to look at ordinary things in a different way.

❑ Grow mould on orange peel and bread, sealed in a plastic bag; or grow cultures on agar. **There is a health and safety consideration here, however, and teachers must be aware of this.** Liaison with a secondary school might bring advice and help with equipment.

❑ After looking at how medical scientists have gone about their research, children could be encouraged to suggest how they would set up their own investigations into problems that involve their health. They can do this in the same spirit as the scientists, and they will be able to see that there are no obvious answers at the outset of an investigation and research and testing do not necessarily come to a neat conclusion. Instead, the scientist may just find more questions!

There is much in this sort of work that can be cross-curricular. It does not attempt to recreate the chronological sequence of events which makes up a life, because much of the scientist's life and work is not 'dramatic': it is painstaking and sometimes lonely. However, such activities should bring home to children how scientists build upon the work of others, and how our lives are affected by the discoveries of many people throughout history and throughout the world.

Subject checklist

Science: learning about germs and antiseptics; the circulation of the blood; microscopes.

Technology: devising sterilising techniques; dressings for wounds.

History: advances in medical history; changes in hospital conditions.

Books

Medical Research Dr Martin Hughes (**Finding Out About** series) Franklin Watts 1990, ISBN 0 7496 0328 3.

Medicine John Aylett (**A Century of Change** series) Hodder & Stoughton 1990, ISBN 0 3404 9942 7.

Medicine (**My first reference library**) Belitha Press 1992, ISBN 0 6201 8556 1.

Pioneers of Science series including *Edward Jenner* ISBN 0 7502 0167 3. Stephen Morris, and *Joseph Lister* 0 7502 0168 1 Douglas McTavish, Wayland 1992.

Software

Acorn Computers Ltd, Fulbourn Road, Cambridge CB1 4JN produces *Medicine: Recent Developments* (Code: 830). Suitable for all Acorn compatible computers.

Script for some germs

Many teachers feel anxious about tackling drama, but a few moments' consideration can be quite reassuring. As teachers, we are acting every day. We are using different voices and different personae to encourage, persuade, illustrate, cajole, harangue and rebuke. Yet however inventive we try to be in discussing work with pupils, they will not remember all their learning. This is where a practical activity such as drama comes in, providing as it does a valuable 'aide-memoire'.

■ A NEW TEACHING TOOL

I did not consider using drama to illustrate scientific learning and help children to absorb it until I was approached by my local science adviser, who said 'Come on Wendy, you're very keen on using drama to aid learning. Will you do a session for teachers showing how drama can be used in science?'

Although I had not thought of using drama in this way before, I was subsequently very pleased that I had been pushed into developing what has proved to be a valuable tool.

From the fourth year onwards at grammar school, I found science very confusing; and I think it was often ill-explained. So I began my consideration of possibilities for science and drama by looking at areas which I had found difficult and working out how drama might have helped me to understand them better. From this starting point, I became quite excited at the potential for drama in the field of science; and I soon had an idea for developing a script as part of a project I was going to do with my new class.

'Weird and Wonderful' was the overall theme I and my colleague, Jan, had chosen for the summer term with the class of mixed-ability first year juniors we were taking as a job-share.

❏ We were going to consider weird and wonderful creatures in children's literature.

❏ We would link all sorts of craft work with this, including sculpture.

❏ The theme would, we hoped, encourage some inventive imaginative writing.

❏ We would look at weird and wonderful machines, and this would give us opportunities for design and technology work, inventing and developing our own machines.

❏ There could be mime and voice orchestration work around the theme of machines.

❏ Finally, we would look at the most marvellous machine of all: the human body. Part of this area of the work would involve a project on teeth.

Improvisation and writing their own plays help lower junior children learn about germs and the need for dental hygiene.

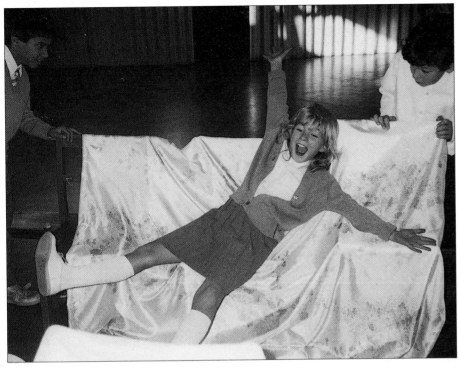

■ BITING INTO 'TEETH'

I visited our local dentist and asked her if she would come to talk to the children. She was too busy to do this, but organised a time for me to go and have a lesson with her about dentists' tools and the jobs they are used for. She would then lend me a set of tools, and I could regurgitate my newly-acquired information to my unsuspecting pupils.

So, armed with a battery of notes, a set of dentists' tools and boxes of dentists' pamphlets about teeth, as well as school science books on the subject, I was ready to begin.

I made a set of worksheets to accompany every pamphlet and book we had. Worksheets for those with reading difficulties were simplified, with limited reading and writing.

The worksheets covered:
- ❏ information about the structure of the mouth and teeth
- ❏ differences between first teeth and second teeth
- ❏ how to look after teeth
- ❏ ways in which we damage our teeth and how we can prevent damage
- ❏ what the dentist can do if we have problems with our teeth
- ❏ which tools are used
- ❏ looking at how animals' teeth are different from people's.

■ THE SCRIPT TAKES SHAPE

As I looked at the problems of plaque in the mouth and the way in which sugar reacts with the bacteria to create harmful acids, I realised the potential for a script. There were parts for lots of bacteria, and they could all have names and talk about their host's mouth. Apart from being instructive, a short piece of drama work might also, in an amusing way, discourage children from eating too many sugary foods and encourage them to ensure that they clean their teeth regularly.

I had never written a script in this way before, and I felt it would be useful to my own development. So the little play 'To the attack' was born. It is reproduced on pages 72 and 73.

After we had, as a class, shared the discoveries that the children had made using the literature and worksheets on teeth, we discussed what caused problems in our mouths. I suggested that some interesting plays could be made up if we gave bacteria characters and they acted out their lives within the mouth. We considered what names they might have and what they might do.

During our weekly drama sessions in the hall, we began to do some improvisation work, which I hoped would lead the children to develop their own plays as well as prepare them for the introduction of my script. Initially, working individually, the children pretended to be germs in a dirty mouth, moving about, exploring, commenting on what they found, moving to different percussive rhythms. Then they worked in pairs, building up conversations with other germs.

■ PROPS AND PLAYS

❑   Following the introductory improvisation work, the children were put into groups of four or five.

❑   At this stage, I put out all sorts of props: PE apparatus, stage boxes, chairs of various shapes, stools and benches, plus pieces of material of varying shape, colour and texture.

❑   Each group used the props to devise a 'mouth'.

❑   Then a leader was appointed to chair discussions in which the group had to come up with a short scene that could take place within the dirty mouth.

❑   Plays were performed simultaneously and refinements made.

❑   To finish, we watched each other's plays and discussed them constructively.

❑   Back in the classroom, groups stayed together and wrote down the plays they had developed. Before writing, we discussed how plays were written and looked at some plays.

During our next drama session in the hall, I introduced my own script. I did this after the children had had the experience of developing a script

themselves, because we could share our experience as writers, having tackled the same task. They had shared their work with me, and I was now showing them my work and asking them to help me by performing it.

■ LOOKING AT DENTISTS' TOOLS

We finished our tooth project with my lesson about dentists' tools. A selection of these was put on each group of tables and the children drew them and wrote about them, swapping with other groups when necessary.

We also looked at toothbrushes and their design; and in addition to this technology work, we brought in mathematics and surveyed the numbers of fillings in the class, looking for any differences between boys and girls. The results of the survey were shown on block graphs, and the work also brought in fractions and percentages.

Finally, the children wrote to our dentist telling her about their discoveries and plays, and enclosing some of their drawings as well as posters about tooth hygiene.

The work I have described took place two years BNC (Before the National Curriculum). However, I believe that you can have fun and still cover the attainment targets, and that drama work such as I have described can help you do this.

Subject checklist
Science: learning about part of the human body; dental care; chemical reactions between food and the body.
Technology: looking at the design of medical implements and toothbrushes; designing and making a 'mouth'; designing and making posters.
Mathematics: using fractions and percentages; collecting information and displaying it in block graph form.
English: writing plays; writing letters.

Books
Germs Make Me Sick Melvin Berger (**First Sight** series) A & C Black 1989, ISBN 0 7136 3092 2.
Healthy Teeth Constance Milburn (**Healthy Living** series) Wayland 1990, ISBN 1 8521 0902 5.
Look at Teeth Henry Pluckrose Franklin Watts 1988, ISBN 0 86313 697 4.
Visiting the Dentist Althea Dinosaur 1990, ISBN 0 8512 2743 0.

Chart
Pictorial Charts Educational Trust, 27 Kirchen Road, London W13 0UD produces *The Development and Care of Teeth* (T50).

Software
Rickitt Educational Media, Ilton, Ilminster, Somerset TA19 9BR supplies *Teeth and Dental Care*. Suitable for BBC 40/80, Archimedes and Nimbus network.

Useful address
British Dental Health Foundation, Eastlands Court, St Peter's Road, Rugby CV21 3QP. Send large SAE for information.

To the attack

(PE apparatus, chairs or stools can form the teeth. Red cloth can be laid on the floor to represent the bottom lip. Pink cloth can represent the gum, and a large tongue-shaped piece of it can represent the tongue. A large cardboard toothbrush or a clean broom can serve as a toothbrush.)

NASTY   Come on everyone! Over the lips into the mouth. This one should be easy! I don't think these teeth saw a toothbrush this morning.

BASHER   Wow! I've found a great slide and there's food hidden all round it - we can have a party! *(BEASTLY appears over the tooth on which Basher is.)*

BEASTLY   Hey! Leave some for me!

BASHER   Oh, don't worry, there's plenty for all. *(BEASTLY joins Basher to eat little bit of food.)*

NASTY   What's this? Mmm. Toast and . . . now let me see . . . Ah! Marmalade. I prefer honey, that's really gooey and sticky, but there, you can't have everything. 'Beggars can't be choosers', as my mother used to say. Mind you, she didn't live it up like we do today. I mean - she hardly ever saw a sweet . . . *(NASTY explores further along the teeth, cartwheeling and jumping, then suddenly stops to prod above a tooth. A HUMAN sighing 'Ooh' and 'Ouch' is heard offstage.)*

BEASTLY   Careful, this gum's a bit sore. Oh! Wait for it! Here comes the tongue - felt me making myself a nuisance I expect. Duck down! *(The material 'tongue' is taken over the teeth as the germs duck down.)*

BASHER   Oh! Oh! I think something bad is going to happen. Have you looked outside recently? Our host is standing at the sink.

BEASTLY and NASTY	Oh no!
BASHER	I thought so! Here comes the brush and . . . what's that on top? Aargh! Our days are numbered - it's fluoride toothpaste! *(The giant 'brush' is swept over the apparatus teeth. The germs tumble, jump and pitch down off the apparatus and lie at the bottom.)*
BEASTLY	Phew! What a ghastly experience!
NASTY	Yeah - it's getting kind of clean around here. I'm all covered in froth!
BASHER	Oh! - Watch out! - Here's some liquid and it's pink and smelly! *(The GERMS shriek and try to protect their faces, curling up and warding off the attack. Then all remain still, except for NASTY.)*
NASTY	Ugh! I think it was mouthwash. I'm feeling rather ill. How are my friends? (He calls.) Beastly . . . Basher . . . Come on, wake up! Oh dear . . . I think they're done for and I feel so weird myself. (He staggers and falls.)
HUMAN	Wow! My mouth feels better now. Gosh, but my gums are sore. I must remember to clean my teeth. I don't want to feel like that again.

Gasping for breath

A programme of drama and research teaches children about hazards to breathing both now and in our industrial past.

We all know what it is like to have our normal breathing interrupted, whether from an asthma attack, holding our breath while swimming underwater, or merely standing at the side of a road full of fumes. Learning Through Action, a group of teachers based in Berkshire, devised their programme, 'Struggling for breath' so that children could use role-play and investigation to examine how we breathe and to contrast the plight and ignorance of Victorian workers in industries which were a hazard to the respiratory system with the knowledge and choices we have in our lives today.

Designed for children working towards National Curriculum Key Stages 2 and 3, the programme was first presented at London's Science Museum by a team of teachers from Learning Through Action; but many elements could easily be adapted by junior and middle school teachers for use in their own classrooms.

■ VICTORIAN HEALTH

At the beginning of the programme, pupils are transported into the past as they witness a Victorian street scene, where a 'quack' doctor selling various dubious bottles which he claims will cure a whole range of illnesses - common and serious - is challenged by a bona fide doctor.

❏ What is really in the little bottles and packets?

❏ What are the huckster's qualifications?

❏ Why should anyone believe that his wares have the power to heal?

The real doctor introduces the subject of health in Victorian times, and goes on to talk about his particular area of interest: lung ailments and the industries that contribute to them.

The scene having been set, the pupils are given the task of looking

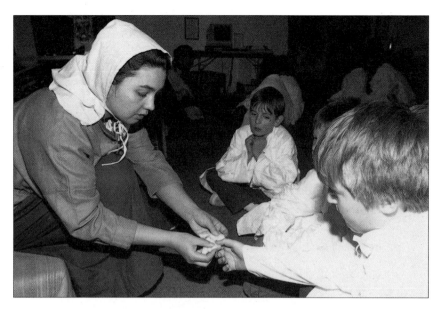

at lung illnesses in Victorian times; how they were caused and how they compare with today's lung diseases. To assist them in their research, they form two groups: one round a Victorian character and one round a contemporary character. Both characters are affected by lung illness.

The Victorian character is Beth, a cotton worker:

'Have you ever been in a mill? The noise is deafening. I mean, if you can imagine two bits of wood banging together as hard as you can right by your ear, that's what it's like!'

The listeners are grabbed by the first few sentences, and that sets the tone for the rest of the storytelling.

■ MILLS THAT KILL AND CIGARETTES

Through a series of anecdotal memories, Beth tells the children about her first arrival at a cotton mill at the age of eight and the sort of work she did, like collecting bobbins and sweeping up the cotton dust.

The children try 'piecing' (re-joining) two broken threads in the few seconds they would have had before machinery trapped their fingers.

A vivid picture of daily life is built up:
the hours and meal times
the relationship between workers
the processes of the job itself.

As they examine raw cotton samples, the children learn how eating and breathing in the cotton dust in large quantities might have dispelled hunger pains, but gradually clogged up the lungs and hindered breathing. They hear how mill owners would spray the cotton with steam to prevent brittle fibres from filling the air, but this created a hot, damp atmosphere which caused further ill-health for the workers, especially in winter. The story is brought to a climax as Beth describes her mother's symptoms; a cough developed into a serious lung condition and finally death.

In contrast, the modern character is Stella, a mother whose son Mark was diagnosed as having asthma at the age of three, and who since then has been learning to cope with his condition.

Stella talks about what triggers Mark's asthma:
pollen
the common cold
smoke.

Stella talks about how Mark takes reasonable care to avoid these triggers and shows the children a **nebulizer** which helps him breathe if he has a bad attack. She also shows them preventative and emergency inhalers, and, like Mark, the pupils measure their 'puff' on a peak flow meter.

As she is talking, Stella is visited by a neighbour, Rosalene, who also

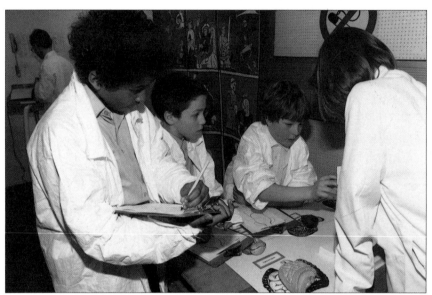

has asthma. Rosalene is having trouble breathing and doesn't have her inhaler. As she begins to recover from her attack, she reaches for a cigarette. Here, the students are made aware of the contrast between Rosalene's attacks, caused by her own failure to take responsibility for her health, and Mark's normal and active life with the aid of regular medication.

This example aims to highlight the problems asthmatics face, yet at the same time dispel fears and misconceptions about these problems, by offering a greater understanding of the facts. Throughout the storytelling, pupils are encouraged to question the character and to relate what they have heard to their own concerns and experiences.

■ STORYTELLING

The storytelling element is vital to any Learning Through Action work. Facts and information are brought to life by being intertwined with personal reminiscences. Mental pictures, which will stay with the children, are created, as characters describe their living and working conditions, and their feelings and attitudes towards these and the people around them.

'Struggling for Breath' introduces four other characters:
❏ a Victorian mineworker whose main focus is the hazards of mining, including gas explosions and the curse of the 'black lung'
❏ a Victorian doctor who describes the living conditions of ordinary people, how diseases are caught, and contemporary cures
❏ a smoker who wants to 'give up', and who explains the effects of smoking and his struggle with an addiction
❏ an ex-asbestos worker who, having worked unprotected in the 1950s with asbestos, now finds he has asbestosis.

A teacher may wish to focus on any of these, as each can stimulate intense discussions; the comparisons between Victorian and modern characters raise such questions as:

❏ What safety precautions do we have in industries today?

❏ Do we know if they are sufficient?

❏ Can we, as individuals, do anything about our polluted environment?

For teachers who are reluctant to tell a story in role, a gentler way in may be **hot seating**, where pupils ask questions of the teacher who is in role as a particular character. Preparing the pupils beforehand by discussing the questions they might ask helps them to gain a greater understanding of the situation, and adds to success.

Alternatively, teachers of older children may set them the task of researching specific Victorian roles, and the rest of the class can then hot seat them. If the teacher takes on a modern role afterwards, this can provide an important contrast.

■ LUNGS AND BREATHING

The second part of the programme involves pupils in further investigations into lungs and breathing. Research areas are set up around the room. The children are encouraged to visit each area and participate in activities.

In a Learning Through Action session, because of the limited time, each activity is supervised by a teacher who can take the pupils through the task. In a classroom situation, however, more time could be allowed for each activity.

Often written instructions are as appropriate as teacher supervision. Or the teacher may wish to focus the class specifically on one activity. The following areas could be modified for classroom use:

❏ **Computers:** Using 'Touch Explorer Plus' to create a concept keyboard overlay. With this, pupils are able to retrieve information selected and stored by the teacher by touching a diagram of a lung. The information includes the names of different parts of the lung and material about lung diseases and treatments.

❏ **Torso model:** Pupils are given an outline of a human torso, and they draw where they think the major body organs are located. They then put together the pieces of a torso model to find out if they are correct. Models can be borrowed from teacher resource centres and university education departments.

❏ **Breathing:** A Victorian corset (or any lace-up corset will do) is used to demonstrate how breathing was restricted (and not just for working women) in the nineteenth century. This brings in the question of how the diaphragm works.

❏ **Exercise:** Using a simple step-test, children can identify the relationship between lungs, pulse rate and fitness.

❏ **Vitalograph:** A pupil's lung capacity may be measured using a vitalograph (borrowed from a local college or university PE department, or from a hospital or health centre), or an asthma peak flow meter. Or,

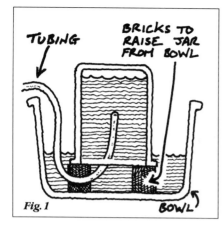

TUBING

BRICKS TO RAISE JAR FROM BOWL

BOWL

Fig. 1

Books
Air Scare Jeremy Leggett (**Operation Earth** series) Heinemann 1991, ISBN 0 4310 0788 8.
Finding out about Industrial Britain Madeline Jones Batsford 1984, ISBN 0 7134 4353 7.
The Lungs and Breathing Brian R. Ward (**The Human Body** series) Franklin Watts 1988, ISBN 0 86313 706 7.

Packs
The National Asthma Campaign, Providence House, Providence Place, London N1 2XX, Tel (071) 226 2260 provides a primary school pack containing pamphlets, leaflets, posters and a comic for children about asthma and its treatment.

Learning Through Action has a pack, 'Getting Better', available from Learning Through Action, Cumberland Road, Reading, Berks, RG1 3JY. Tel: (0734) 665556.

Video
Educational Media International, 235 Imperial Drive, Rayners Lane, Harrow, Middlesex HA2 7HE produces Be Smart . . . Don't Start Smoking.

alternatively, an experiment can be set up to displace water using a bell jar, a tank and some rubber tubing (see Fig. 1). The person with the largest lung capacity is the one who can blow the water down to the lowest mark on the bell jar.

Having measured lung capacity, further work on the relationship between height, weight, fitness and lung capacity can then be undertaken.

❏ **Asthma:** Pupils are shown examples of medication used by asthmatics and given advice on how to react if they see someone having an attack.

Using a simple set of illustrated cards, pupils discuss whether statements like 'If you suffer from asthma, you should not keep pets' are true or false.

❏ **Microscopes:** Microscopes, set up to show slides of different dusts and fibres like animal hair, pollen etc. provide children with the opportunity to draw, compare and comment on what they see.

❏ **Resusci Ann** Mouth to mouth resuscitation can be demonstrated using a Resusci Ann. Courses in this method are provided by St John's Ambulance, who may be willing to send someone to talk to a class.

❏ **Smoking** Display and video materials designed to combat smoking can be obtained from ASH (Action on Smoking and Health).

At the end of the programme, the children are gathered in a forum session where they can share their experiences. They may bring artefacts of interest or findings from their own research. Issues and further questions are often raised at this point, and invariably the comparison between Victorian and modern-day experiences leads to a discussion on avoidable and unavoidable hazards and the control we have over our own health.

The discussion of issues at the forum session often acts as a stimulus for further research in the classroom or library. Thus, while aiming to fulfil National Curriculum objectives in science and other subjects, 'Struggling for Breath', like other Learning Through Action programmes, acts as a springboard to further investigation. Learning is a continuous process in which there is always room for further action.

Subject checklist
Science: learning about the lungs; what keeps lungs healthy and what threatens them; air pollution.
Technology: finding out about ways of limiting air pollution (from industry or smoking).
Information technology: retrieving information for research.
History: comparing nineteenth-century medicine and nineteenth-century industrial conditions with today's.

Contributors

KEN BYRON lectures in the Faculty of Education at the University of Central England in Birmingham

MIKE POTTER teaches at the National Junior School, Nottingham

ROS SMITH teaches at Great Waltham Primary School, Chelmsford

JULIE HAWKSBY and **IRENE HESELTINE** are drama consultants for Cleveland

MIKE LITTLEDYKE lecturers in the Faculty of Education and Health at Cheltenham and Gloucester College of Higher Education

DAVID WORLEY works at Marwell Zoological Park, Hampshire

The members of **LEARNING THROUGH ACTION** are seconded teachers from Berkshire

NICK FOLKARD teaches at Colet Court School, which is the preparatory department of St Paul's School, London

WENDY ALLEN teaches at St Richard with St Andrew's School, Richmond

All contributions were originally published in the magazine **Questions:** EXPLORING SCIENCE & TECHNOLOGY 3-13.

Questions is published eight times a year by
The Questions Publishing Company
6/7 Hockley Hill, Hockley
Birmingham B18 5AA
Tel. 021 507 0850.

Index

A

Animals 37, 38, 43-46, 69
Antiseptics 63-65
Asbestos 76
Asthma 74-78

B

Blood transfusion 63-67

C

Caves 8-11, 37
Cigarettes (see 'Smoking')
Clothing 9, 38, 43, 52, 65
Community life 26-30, 31-35, 36-41, 54-60
Conservation 31-35, 36-41, 42-48

D

Dentistry 68-73
Drew, Charles 65-67

E

Economic awareness 26-30, 31-35, 36-40, 45-46, 50-53
Exploration 8-12, 36-40, 42-46

F

Families 31-34, 36-40, 50-53
Farming 50-53
Food 36-40, 50-53
Fortifications 13

G

Geology 8-11, 19, 20-24, 36-40
Germs 54-57, 61-2, 63-67, 68-73
Government (local) 26-30, 31-34, 54-57
Gravestones 20-23

I

Industry 26-30, 31-34, 50-53, 74-78

L

Lister, Joseph 64-65
Local government (see 'Government')
Lungs 74-78

M

Maps 10, 17, 27, 29, 32, 37, 43, 54-60
Matchmaking 50-53
Medicine 54-57, 61-62, 63-67, 74-78
Minerals 8-11, 13-17, 19, 20-24, 36-40
Mining 50-53

N

Newspapers 31-34, 36-40
Nineteenth century 50-53, 54-57, 63-67, 74-78

P

Pasteur, Louis 54, 64-65
Plants 36-40, 42-46
Pollution 26-30, 31-34, 54-57
Potholing 8-11

R

Religion 36-40
Roads 13-18, 31-34
Romans (Ancient) 13-17

S

Smoking 74-78

T

Teeth 68-73
Textile manufacture 50-53, 74-78
Tourism 36-40
Traffic 31-34
Tribes 36-40

W

Waste 26-30, 31-34, 54-57
Water supply 26-30, 54-57